LOVE
your body

or how to be a live food lover

Viktoras Kulvinskas, M.S.
former director of research
Hippocrates Health Institute

*Send this book to
someone you love!*

21st Century Publications
P.O. 702
Fairfield, Iowa 52556

Introduction

In chapter thirteen of his first letter to the Corinthians, Paul extols the virtues of "love." Paul says that prophetic powers, a complete understanding of all mysteries and all wisdom and knowledge, even faith are all meaningless without love. "Love is patient and kind," writes Paul, "love is not jealous or boastful; it is not arrogant or rude. Love does not insist on its own way; it is not irritable or resentful; it does not rejoice at wrong, but rejoices in the right. Love bears all things, believes all things, hopes all things, endures all things . . . So faith, hope, love abide, these three; but the greatest of these is love."

Viktoras Kulvinskas very wisely and appropriately has entitled this excellent little book LOVE YOUR BODY. If the greatest human quality is love, then certainly the most marvelous human POSSESSION is one's own body! Remember when Jesus was asked what was the greatest commandment in all the law? He answered, "You should love God with all your heart, mind, soul and strength, and your fellow human being as yourself." There's more to that summary than meets the eye.

If you truly love God, you will love and respect God's marvelous creation, the human body. If you love yourself, that is, if you love yourself to the extent of treating your own body as the temple it is, then a love of your fellow human beings will naturally flow. A clean, healthy body - the result of a proper diet and fasting - will produce a pure, moral state of mind which will certainly overflow into human relationships. If you eat right and treat your body right, you will display those qualities which Paul describes in writing about love.

Most folks today neither LOVE nor KNOW their bodies. The average person has no idea of the LOCATION of the organs, glands, vessels, nerves, arteries and other parts of the body, to say nothing of a lack of knowledge of their FUNCTION. Most folks go through life as though they truly believed the opening words of that old song: "I ain't got no BODY!"

The American Dream is to work very hard to earn enough money. or establish enough credit to surround yourself with pieces of machinery - a television set, a refrigerator, a dishwasher, a stereo, a clothes washer and dryer, and, of course, an automobile. But before you've earned a penny, Mother Nature has provided you free of charge with the most marvelous piece of machinery you will ever own - your own body. Yet most folks appreciate this marvelous piece of equipment and priceless possession the least!

It is sad to say that most folks treat their automobiles better than their own bodies. Which means, of course, they love their automobiles more! They're more concerned about the "Ford in their future" than whether or not they'll have a future to put a Ford into! For example, if it was definitely proved that smoking cigarettes inside an automobile would instantly corrode the engine, all smokers would quit smoking inside their cars! No car owner would pour refined sugar into the gas tank, or stuff a steak in the carburetor, or shove wet, soggy white bread into the radiator. Car owners wouldn't dream of doing such things because they know it would damage their precious machines.

Moreover, car owners constantly search for the best possible fuel for their cars. They are careful to change the oil regularly and see that the car is periodically lubricated. They carefully read the owner's manual provided by the manufacturer of the automobile to make sure they are treating their machine correctly. Yet the same car owner will park the automobile, run into a luncheonette and completely ruin his or her body by the kind of so-called "food" consumed.

This book should serve as an owner's manual for everyone who has the good sense to love their bodies as their finest and proudest possessions. Each page is packed with condensed, clear, concise wisdom and truth. It has been provided with love and concern for your very life by author Viktoras Kulvinskas, and it is undoubtedly the most important book you will ever read.

Peace be with you.

Dick Gregory
February 1974

ACKNOWLEDGEMENT

I want to express my appreciation to Professor Edmond Bordeaux Szekely for his permission to quote from the beautiful translation Essene Gospel of Peace (Academy Press, 3085 Reynard Way, San Diego, Ca 92103). The original manuscripts of the teachings of Jesus on the healing forces of nature exist in Aramaic in the archives of the Vatican and in the old Slavonic in the Royal Archives Hapsburg.

— contents —

— recipes —

— appendix —

Fruit ... Apples ... Avocado ... Grapes ...
Lemon ... Melon ... Millet ... Wheat ...
Legumes ... Mung Sprouts ... Alfalfa
Sprouts ... Soybean ... Nuts ... Cashew ...
Sesame Seed ... Sunflower Seed

— foreword —

Love your body the live food organic way. We can treat ourselves with love and become more healthy and more beautiful. Through right diet, we can slim the body, rejuvenate it, make it youthful. Children born from such parents will know endless youth, beauty and total freedom from disease. They will love everybody.

This recipe book is right for our synthetic unnatural age. It is written for survival. There are many books on the market filled with recipes heavenly in the mouth and hell in the stomach. My emphasis is upon preparing, from live food, tasty simple colorful combinations in harmony with the physiological limitations of the body.

— introduction —

Today, unless you isolate yourself high in the tropical mountains, you are very likely breathing polluted air and eating poisoned food. Our civilization encourages through advertisement and education many practices which make the human body sick and ugly. The marketplace carries more than 5000 items processed from wholesome food. They are non-foods. The wholesome nutrients have been removed and replaced with synthetic, poisonous chemicals. A supermarket diet has helped to create the sickest nation on this planet.

More than 60% of Americans (20% of the youth under 17) are suffering from a chronic disorder. They are the medicated incurables. All the others, with the exception of those who are using a simple vegetarian diet, are self-medicated with laxatives, aspirin, sleeping pills, tranquilizers, pep pills, alkalizers, deodorants, alcohol.

Research at the Hippocrates Health Institute has shown that pollution of the bloodstream from careless eating affects the health more than the air we breathe. The emphasis in this book is upon a low starch, low protein, low fat, raw food diet. Sprouts and indoor greens are high in enzymes, vitamins, alkaline minerals and chlorophyl, providing all the nutrients needed by the body.

"No one knows what he can do till he tries."

Our research, and research published in many medical journals (read **Survival Into The 21st Century**) clearly shows that such food has great protective value in a toxic environment. It can regenerate a sick body into a healthy one, and can maintain life in superb health.

This is a spiritual age. It beats in the hearts of many of the young and their elders. The spiritual nature of man requires an unpolluted temple through which to perfect itself.

"He who is slave to his belly seldom worships God."

— Saadi

When one eats a heavy meal, his energy goes from head to stomach. Some people even pass out. In the Bible, fasting is mentioned as often as prayer. God consciousness is not achieved on a full stomach. Frugal eating is important. It produces a spiritually receptive, strong and healthy body. On a live food diet you eat about one-fourth the amount you eat on a devitalized food diet.

The discipline of Yoga requires a flexible body. Cooked food, salt, dairy products and excessive use of concentrated food (nuts, seed, grain, oil, dried fruit, avocado, sea vegetables) congest the cells, joints and blood stream. In time it stiffens the body, robbing it of youth.

"The Kingdom of God will come upon the earth when there shall be neither male nor female among you."

— Jesus

Most spiritual disciplines require total or partial chastity. On a low protein, live food diet continence becomes an easy discipline. Continence conserves important nutrients, making the body stronger and more flexible for asanas and meditation.

Inclusion in the diet of sprouted grains, sprouted seed and nuts helps to maintain sexual vitality. They will replenish many of the nutrients lost during intercourse. To insure many years of vitality, one should practice continence as often as he can to give the body time to rejuvenate itself. In the United States, many men become impotent by the age of 40. The Hunzas, who live naturally, father children at ages well beyond 100.

The female's rate of growth of mind and body slows down dramatically as soon as menstruation begins. The menstrual flow robs her of nutrients needed for brain and body development. The more toxic the body, the longer and more difficult the menstrual period. In a detoxified body, it would be reduced to a clear flow lasting no more than an hour.

If a live food diet were introduced on a large scale, the threat of population explosion would be reduced to a nightmare from the past. Couples would be guided in reproduction by rational, economic and spiritual considerations. There would be no undesired children. All disease would disappear. The lifespan would be extended to hundreds of years.

Man's physiology requires a frugal live food diet which incorporates periods of fasting to keep the body in a continuously detoxified state. Such a diet will eliminate doctor's bills and the need to carry expensive insurance. It will simplify your life style; you will not have to spend many hours in the wasteful, destructive act of cooking.

These recipes place a great emphasis on food that is organic and readily available to all. You can reduce your total food bill up to 80%. Yes, you can live organically on a sprouts-indoor greens diet for 10 cents a day, or up to 69 cents, if you include seed, nuts, avocado, fruits, vegetables. The seed and fruit can be bought in bulk; they have excellent keeping quality.

You may have to retrain your taste buds. Many years of hot, spicy, cooked food may have degenerated them. A live food diet can bring them back to activity. Then you will be ready to enjoy natural foods.

You can change your life now by adopting the optimum nutritional regime outlined in this book. Continuously simplify your eating habits; eventually discontinue the use of all extraneous tools, electric utensils and spices.

As your body becomes purified, it will demand a more simple diet. Sprouts, seed, indoor greens and a few leaves of sea vegetable will provide a complete, filling meal. An apple, a peach or a slice of melon will be a satisfying meal.

In a poisoned environment, one needs the healing and protective power of greens and sprouts. In a natural setting, man can return to his natural diet—fruit. Ezekiel said, "And the fruit thereof shall be for meat, and the leaf thereof for medicine."

Until we meet in the Garden of Eden,

Love One Another,

Viktoras

"Renew yourselves and fast. For I tell you truly, that Satan and his plagues may only be cast out by fasting and by prayer. Go by yourself and fast alone, and show your fasting to no man. The living God shall see it and great shall be your reward. And fast till Beelzebub and all his evils depart from you, and all the angels of our Earthly Mother come and serve you. For I tell you truly, except you fast, you shall never be freed from the power of Satan and from all diseases that come from Satan. Fast and pray fervently, seeking the power of the living God for your healing. While you fast, eschew the Sons of Men and seek our Earthly Mother's angels, for he that seeks shall find."

—The Essene Gospel of Peace,
Prof. Edmond Szekely

WHY VEGETARIAN?

Man's basic physiology has not changed in millions of years. He still has the digestive tract of a fruitarian animal (gorilla). There is no significant similarity between man and meat-eating animals. Man has made an evolutionary error by introducing into his diet animal products and cooked food.

"Comparative anatomy teaches us that man resembles the frugivorous ape in everything, the carnivorous in nothing...It is only by softening and disguising dead flesh by culinary preparation that it is rendered susceptible to mastication or digestion, and that the sight of its bloody juices and raw horror does not excite loathing and disgust."
— Shelley, A Vindication of Natural Diet

Meat and Eggs are not healthful foods. They are high in cholesterol. Excessive use of heated, medicated animal products causes toxic waste products of protein metabolism and putrefaction in the intestine to be stored in the body, leading to degenerative diseases, (heart disorders, cancer, leukemia, gout).

Dairy Products: After weaning, milk is no longer necessary in the diet. Dairy products are mucus-inducing, loaded with chemicals, and difficult to digest once pasteurized and/or combined with other foods. Many people are allergic to them. They are one of the main causes of colds, respiratory disorders, artery degeneration.

Experiment in Body Ecology: For one month, abstain from all animal products. Replace them with raw and cooked vegetarian dishes. At the end of this period, prepare yourself a meal typical what you formerly ate. Devastating effects will be quickly evident. Unless the meal is followed by coffee, you will experience lack of energy, heaviness of body and mental stupor. After 30 days abstinence from dairy products, milk, yogurt or cheese will generally induce all the symptoms of a cold. These undesirable effects are more convincing than all the arguments for vegetarianism. You have a choice. You can be a dead food addict with resultant poor health, or you can become a vegetarian and experience the joy of living.

FOOD COMBINING FOR GOOD DIGESTION

Most people suffer digestive disorders. Many are being treated for them and others experience symptoms of indigestion, lack of vigor, pallor, headaches, dizziness, insomnia or a need for many hours of sleep, unknowing of the cause.

Indigestion stems from anxiety, highly processed food, eating hurriedly, reducing the concentration of digestive juices with fluids, eating excessively and not chewing food thoroughly. The biggest villain is serving two concentrated foods that are hard to digest at the same meal.

Man's digestive tract was not made to be the receptacle for an eight course meal containing a wide array of poisons. As long as body vitality is high, you can lead the life of a gourmet. In time, bouts of indigestion become more frequent.

The typical combination of meat, potatoes, butter or margarine, a glass of milk along with an array of highly processed carbohydrates (bread, pastries), has produced the sickest nation on this planet.

Protein requires acid digestive juices, while starch and sweet food require alkaline. You cannot digest both at the same time. Dairy products are highly alkaline, so they interfere with meat digestion. Fat interferes with protein digestion.

Poorly combined food remains too many hours in the digestive tract. In this warm environment it rots and/or ferments, producing a wide range of poisons, headache, and an unloving disposition.

Vegetables take longer to digest than fruit; combining them in a single meal can cause fermentation.

I have included charts of food combinations compatible with the physiological limitations of the body, also suggestions for promoting good digestion. If you listen to your body, you will discover that these food combinations are best for good digestion and vitality.

WHY UNFIRED FOODS?

"Men of Sattwa like foods which increase their vital force, energy, strength and health. Such foods add to the physical and mental life. They are juicy, soothing, fresh and agreeable. But men of Rajas prefer foods which are violently bitter, sour, salty, hot, pungent, acid and burning. These cause ill health, and distemper of the mind and body. And men of Tamas take a perverse pleasure in foods which are stale, tasteless, rotten and impure. They like to eat the leavings of others."

— Bhagavad - Gita

Live Foods for Health and Economy:

Organic live food is your best medicare, your ticket to prolonged youth. Eat natural food which appeals to you most. Advance your diet according to the dictates of your body, the type of work you do. Only the subconscious knows your true needs. Forget charts, tables, nutritionists, they are only for civilized food addicts. Do not use the teeth to crush hard food. If hard to masticate, it is forbidden.

Nature's foods are in their most nutritious state when eaten raw, picked ripe from orchard or garden. Cooking destroys all enzymes, lecithin, many vitamins and much of the protein. As much as 85% of the original nutrients may be lost in cooking.

On a raw food diet, you get a higher nutrient value from your food, hence you eat less. Considering that there is an overpopulation problem, so many people starving, it is a crime against humanity to cook food.

Many air pollutants inhibit enzyme activity in your digestive tract. They destroy a good percentage of vitamins, A, B, C, E, K. Hence it is important to eat food which is high in enzymes and vitamins.

By the time one is 30, because of a diet of heated, dead food, the enzyme concentration in the body's tissues has been reduced by 30 to 50 percent. One could be eating a nutritious diet but it will not be digested unless it contains a sufficient concentration of enzymes. Sprouts will rebuild the enzyme level in the human cell.

TOXEMIA--CAUSE OF DISEASE

A. Carrel, Nobel Prize recipient states: "The cell is immortal. It is merely the fluid in which it floats that degenerates. Renew this fluid at proper intervals, and give the cell proper nourishment upon which to feed, and so far as we know the pulsation of life may go on forever"

– Man The Unknown

Accumulated waste contributes to enervation of the toxic body, eventually manifesting as acute or chronic disease. An acute symptom is merely the body's attempt to cleanse itself.

As you begin on the natural path, do not be surprised when your body starts housecleaning.

Symptoms of nausea, headache, fever and cramps may appear during the first few days. Plenty of rest is vital during this period to give your body a chance to cleanse itself of toxins stored in cells and fatty tissues--the accumulation of a lifetime of wrong food, medication, anger or other abuses of the body.

FOR TRANSITION TO A HEALTHFUL DIET

Health can be restored and/or maintained by eating nutritionally, frugally, pleasurably.

First, cut out sugar, dairy products, white bread and bakery products, all carbonated drinks, hamburgers, hot dogs, snack foods, canned or processed foods, salt and other strong condiments, vinegar, coffee, ice cream, alcohol and cigarettes.

Cut down on the size of meals and combine foods correctly.

Eliminate, or cut down the use of meat to fewer and fewer days a week. Replace it with cooked sprouts, grains and vegatables loaves. Cut down your total protein intake.

If no experience in fasting, skip breakfast several times a week. After a month of improved diet, fast on water or fruit one day a week. Initially fasting is not so important. Improvement in your living habits, elimination of the worst foods and an increase in live foods should be your major concern.

If you have many discomforts during the dietary transition, you can slow down the detoxification by eating more of the cooked foods or by assisting your body through improved elimination; enemas, herbal tonics, showers, skin brushing [for more details read Survival Into The 21st Century].

At times, you will slip back into old habits. On such occassions enjoy [or suffer] the experience in full consciousness and be a witness to how it effects you; discover the origins of such unconscious desires and learn from the teachings. Be grateful for all experiences; do not judge your self and when ready return to the life path as a wiser being. After a binge give at least six hours or much more for natural hunger to return. Use only water or herbal teas if truly thirsty, then re-establish patterns that give you the freedom to be happy on all levels.

Progressively improve your habits until you are on at least an 80% live food diet. The most important focus should be to eat or drink only when the stomach is empty, keeping in mind that most meals require three to six hours to digest. This is the most dangerous abuse. Food incompletely digested rots and/or ferments into poisons making you feel weak and dizzy, look pale, suffer migraines and other pains and need long hours of sleep.

The best diet for city living, should be at least 70% live foods, heavy on sprouts and greens for extra protein and calories, and protection of the respiratory tract. Make regular use of sprouted seed milks or creams, as well as chewing on grass. On a diet of sprouts, indoor greens (buckwheat, wheat, sunflower) seed creams and kelp you can supply all the body's nutritional needs for as little as 20 cents per day.

In a more favorable environment, subtropic, away from the polluted city, a fruit diet with green juice is best.

Improve your oxygen intake; practice yoga in the early morning hours, before the city smog has reached its height from the morning traffic. No one can breathe too much good air

THE DIVINE

"A man who is born with tendencies toward the divine, is fearless and pure in heart. He perseveres in the path to union with Brahman which the scriptures and teachers have taught him. He is charitable. He can control his passions. He studies the scriptures regularly, and obeys their directions. He practices spiritual disciplines. He is straightforward, truthful and of an even temper. He harms no one. He renounces the things of this world. He has tranquil mind and an unmalicious tongue. He is compassionate toward all. He is not greedy. He is gentle and modest. He abstains from useless activity. He has faith in the strength of his higher nature. He can forgive and endure. He is clean in thought and act. He is free from hatred and pride."

— Bhagavad - Gita

Form small groups for the purpose of the study of spiritual wisdom, practice forgiveness for self and others. Eliminate all fear, pain and sorrow by sharing yourself totally with at least one person. Peace, love and freedom from all disease will be your experience.

Make plans to leave the city as soon as your spirit is ready. Gather similarly attuned individuals into a family consciousness unit, seek out land that is at least 100 miles from major city and ecological wastelands, learn to live together, respect the land, earn a livlihood and grow in Oneness.

FOR BEST DIGESTION

When to Eat

Eat only when hungry, after the previous meal has left the stomach. No snacks between meals.

A day will not be wasted on a small (or no) breakfast. Eat the biggest meal at noon when sun activity is strongest. Solar vibrations aid digestion. Eat a small meal before sunset, for a longer night of fasting.

Never eat when in pain, emotionally upset, extremely tired or immediately before or after hard work.

For those with delicate digestion, lie down for at least 10 minutes before a meal. Rest, or relax, after a meal for 45 minutes.

Before a difficult physical or mental task, center your energy and fast on juice or water.

How to Eat

Begin with the name of God; be grateful and ask for control of appetite.

Bring a tranquil mind to meals. Do not argue or rush. Enjoy the music of birds and brook, silence of sky. Enjoy your food.

Eat slowly and chew each mouthful at least 50 times, reducing to fluid before swallowing. Breathe long and deep with each mouthful.

Do not drink or eat cold or hot (beyond 104°) substances.

No liquids with meals. Drink at least 20 minutes before, or three hours after a meal.

One food at a meal, or combine food correctly for best digestion.

Eat juicy foods prior to concentrated foods.

Eat raw foods before cooked foods.

Stop eating before you feel full—no more than 16 oz. at a single meal.

Never encourage anyone to eat.

HOW TO CHOOSE FOODS

To avoid pesticides and other poisons, it's best to grow your own garden, to purchase locally from someone who farms organically or from a reliable natural food store.

Weeds (from an unsprayed area) are higher in nutritional value than cultivated greens. Dandelion, purslane, lambsquarters, red root, nettle, plantain, chickweed, milkweed, thistle, grass are readily available. Most of them will provide tender greens throughout the growing season if you clip them to permit growth.

Leafy Greens are most nutritious when young and tender.

Fruit is best tree or vine-ripened. It is less nutritious when over-ripe. When under-ripe its acids can erode tooth enamel. Fruit from abandoned orchards is unsprayed.

Oils must be cold pressed from organically grown produce.

HOW TO GET STONED ON WATER

"Don't worry...be happy."

Meher Baba

According to government figures over fifty percent of tap water fails to meet minimum standards. The purification process for tap water introduces 20 to 60 new chemicals into your drink. Sodium floride (rat poison) and chlorine (bleach) destroy cells and age your body prematurely. Additives and polluted water are one of the causes for epidemics of flu, indigestion, diarrhea, hepatitis, and 'mono'.

The 'pure' water that one may drink from ring, lake, river, filtered, well or running stream is one of the major factors in producing cemented joints of arthritis; gall and kidney stones; hardening of the arteries and the brain.

As we live longer, we build up inorganic sedimentary deposits in the pipes and filters and eliminative organs of the body. At birth the baby is about 75% water, by the time you reach age 30, the percentage of water in the body is about 55%. Where did the water go? It was displaced by the accumulation of precipitated minerals in the bloodstreams of your body.

It is physiologically impossible for your body to assimilate inorganic minerals in the building of healthy tissue and blood. Calcium carbonate (lime) and other minerals will cement your body. If it was not for the high activity of the eliminative organs, most individuals by the age of forty would have accumulated enough cement in their bodies to make statue replicas of self.

A diet which includes inorganic minerals, concentrated foods (seeds, sea vegetables, dried fruit) or cooked food will necessitate the drinking of fluid. Best is the juice from fruit or vegetables. Distilled water, although preferable over other water forms, has a slight tendency of drawing calcium, and other nutrients, from teeth, bones and cells. By soaking dried or fresh fruit (or vegetables), seed (alfalfa, wheat, fenugreek) or crushed grass overnight, the leeching affect of distilled water can be eliminated. The soaking introduces nutrients into water and converts the dead distilled water into live juice. Such water will help to flush out accumulated poison from bloodstream and cells.

You can get the sand out of your body. It will be dissolved through the persistent application of the following program: (1) Change your water to pure H20 (distilled), (2) Eat little and only live food, (3) Eat a salt free diet, (4) Reduce the use of high mineral foods–sea vegetables, tubers, and grains, (5) Eat no Dairy products, (6) Eat non-acid producing foods, (7) Sun and Exercise.

INDOOR GARDENING

Buckwheat greens – 7 days old

Grow your own food in your home. An indoor garden can provide all the necessary foods for winter (or summer) at least 70% sprouts plus seven day greens. From organically grown seed, you can grow sprouts and salad greens to provide a varied menu.

Sprouts and greens at an early stage of growth are the most live foods available. They are still growing at the dinner table. Although raw food is best, those who are not ready for a completely raw diet, may add raw sprouts to all cooked dishes just before serving. Even this will soon result in important improvement in health.

Seeds prior to sprouting, are generaly hard and have a high starch content--undesirable as food unless they are cooked and seasoned. Sprouting converts the seed into desirable food in a period of 3 to 7 days.

You can grow your own organic garden wherever you are–in any room, in your backpack or jacket pocket, or in your car. Sprouts and indoor greens can reduce the cost of a total organic food diet by 70%.

Sprouting

Wash about one quarter cup of seed. Soak in any wide mouth jar (or any other container--for large quantities, I use plastic buckets or enamel roasting pans), using one part seed to at least two parts water. Soak alfalfa 6 hours (2 tablespoons per quart jar) and mung and lentil 16 hours. Drain off the water. No more soaking. Cover the jar loosely with a cloth and keep in a warm, dark place (about 75° F). Rinse the seed at least twice a day. After three days of rinsing, mung and lentil are ready to eat.

For the sweetest, juiciest mung sprouts, keep the temperature at 80-90° and rinse 3-4 times a day.

Soybeans sprout more readily if the seed are not too old. Soak them 8-10 hours in a cool place. Then put them in a cool place (about 65° F.) and rinse often. They are ready in 3-5 days.

3 tablespoons of alfalfa fill a 2 quart jar in 6 days

After three days of sprouting, place alfalfa in light to induce formation of chlorophyl. At this stage the sprouts must be in a fairly cool place, loose (not densely packed) in the jars to avoid spoilage. In 3 more days, they re ready to eat.

Alfalfa is found to be sensitive to the polluted tap water. It might not sprout. In that case, you definitely should use distilled water, or sprout the alfalfa with other seed, such as: mung, lentil, fenugreek. Sprouted in the same jar all the seed will flourish and provide you a delicious salad.

Comments: The soak water of all the seed is rich in water-soluble minerals and vitamins.

Alfalfa and fenugreek soak water make a delicious tea.

Nutritional changes in the sprouted seed: starch is converted to simple sugars, and protein into amino acids, hence sprouts are a predigested food, easily and completely assimilated by the body.

Vitamin and enzyme content increase tremendously.

A very economical food; one pound of seed can be converted to six pounds of sprouts. For a nutritionally complete meal, sprout a mixture of alfalfa, sunflower, mung and lentil. In three days, serve as a salad with a little sea vegetable (kelp or dulse) and a dash of lemon.

Indoor Greens

These greens are grown on one inch of soil and are ready to eat in seven days. Obtain from the natural food store sproutable wheat, black, unhulled buckwheat, unhulled sunflower, radish or fenugreek seed. Soak the wheat 15 hours, the buckwheat 3 hours, the others 8 hours. Fill a baking pan (or any other flat tray) with dark, porous soil. Fifty percent peat moss will make the soil more porous. Mix in a tablespoon of kelp fertilizer (optional). Moisten the soil--no puddles. Spread the seed next to one another. Cover loosely with a plastic sheet. Put in a warm place. After three days remove the cover. Place the tray in the light. Water as needed. After four additional days it is ready to eat--an economical source of sun-vibrations during the cold winter.

The soil may be replaced with 4 layers of wet cheese cloth or one layer white cotton towel. It is very important to keep towels wet and the pan in a warm place, especially during the first 3 days.

Wheatgrass: Chew on it, sucking in the juice, spitting out the pulp. If you have a special juicer you may extract 10 ounces of juice from one pound of grass (this requires ¼ pound of seed in planting). Cut it fine for salads or blended preparations, or it may be added to all cooked foods. A complete food, wheatgrass is high in chlorophyll which is a good body builder and protective food for city living.

Buckwheat and Sunflower: Remove any remaining husks and use as salad greens. Or juice them. Rich in amino acids, enzymes, vitamins, chlorophyll, low in fat, free from starch.

Fenugreek and Radish: Tangy seasoning for exotic sprout salads. Strong liver cleansers.

All the seeds can also be sprouted and grown without soil.

Potting

In the fall, pot at least one dozen comfrey roots in tall tin cans. Drop in a few earthworms, add some kelp fertilizer and place them in a sunny window. Water as needed. with soak (or rinse) water from your sprouts. The leaves may be harvested continuously.

Comfrey is a valuable nutritious, healing plant. Use the leaves for salads, sauces, tea, or steam them lightly. It is sometimes used as a specific for healing. It is laxative, may be used as a poultice for wounds and chest ailments; hot comfrey tea may be drunk at bedtime to induce sweating.

USEFUL SUGGESTIONS

Chewing is so important. Thorough chewing reduces the consistency of food to permit surface contact with the digestive enzymes that they may carry out its conversion.

All nuts and seed should be chewed to a milk. All vegetables and fruits must be chewed thoroughly to break down the cellulose walls surrounding the nutrients.

For those unable or unwilling to chew their food thoroughly,

Health Fountain Juicer is a specially designed juicer for juicing wheatgrass efficiently. As the juice runs into a glass, the dry pulp is ejected. It can be used also for juicing all leafy greens, sprouts, indoor greens, and for grinding sesame, sunflower, pumpkin seed, nuts and dried fruit.

Blender is useful for making fruit or green drinks, seed sauces and milk. Nuts and seed are probably most digestible when blended to a milk.

Moulinex Grinder (or equivalent hand mill) reduces nuts and seed to a fine meal, or to a thick butter.

Centrifugal or Press Juicer juices all types of fruit and vegetables for a therapeutic liquid diet.

Rainbow Cloudburst Manual Juicer for all non leafy vegetables and fruit. Can extract within two minutes up to 10 ounces of juice from one pound of produce. Weighs 8 ounces. It can also be used for grating all hard vegetables to a fine pulp. Obtain the units locally or write to 21st Century Products, P.O. 702, Fairfield, Iowa 52556.

WHY SEASONING?

Fresh organically grown foods are high in flavor, a delight to the palate. You can learn to enjoy them without seasoning.

Inorganic Salt is not a food; it is not utilized by the body. Some of it is retained, causing stiffening of the joints, arthritis, hardening of the arteries and kidney disease. Eating grains encourages the craving for salt. In a high enough concentration it inhibits cell metabolism, eventually causing their death. In trying to reduce the concentration of salt, your body will only retain an excess of water in the tissues.

Sea Salt or Tamari, Miso (fermented seeds and salt) may be substituted for the supermarket salt. They should be used sparingly.

Vegetable Seasoning (sometimes called broth powder) is a substitute for salt. But be careful in choosing-- it sometimes contains artificial coloring and flavoring and a filler of brewer's yeast and soybeans which might combine poorly with other foods.

Seaweed is the best choice for salty taste. Kelp is a good protective food--it contains all the trace minerals from the sea, and has been shown to prevent absorption of strontium 90 into the body. Dulse leaves are delicious. Salts occur in these sea plants in a form which is easily assimilated.

Herbs used with discrimination can subtly enhance the flavor of food. Pick them fresh from your garden. In winter, grow them in pots on your window sill.

Garlic, Onion, Cayenne, Chili, Ginger Root are noted for healing qualities when one is eating a cooked food diet. They provide flavor for the transitional diet; however, once the body is detoxified, they can act as irritants to kidneys, liver and mucous lining of the digestive tract.

THE IDEAL DIET

The ideal diet can be therapeutic--cleansing and rebuilding, as well as a maintenance diet for health, youth and longevity.

You may advance in a transitional diet at your own pace. Stay on it as long as you need.

The live food diet presented here is very simple, both in menu and in recipes. Most important is to avoid hard-to-digest combinations. You must experiment for yourself.

"The scanty evidence that has survived from the remote past shows that modern man has slowly descended through the five stages: breatharianism, liquidarianism, fruitarianism, vegetarianism, carnivorism."

– Man's Higher Consciousness

Ideally, we would eat a fruit mono (one food at a meal) diet, and use no utensils in preparation. However, for ease in digestion and to entice the appetite, I offer recipes to use until you become a fruitarian.

While living in a polluted environment, for survival one can use a mucuslean diet of sprouts, green juice, fruit and steamed non-starchy vegetables (during transition). Acid fruit (tomatoe, pineapple, citrus) should be used in moderation or else (because of unripeness and personal toxemia) they can contribute to rapid tooth decay and anemia.

WHEATGRASS THERAPY

If the body is in urgent need of cleansing and rebuilding, I suggest adopting immediately the wheatgrass therapy, which is thoroughly explained in **Survival Into The 21st Century**.

The solid content of wheatgrass juice is up to 70% chlorophyll. Chlorophyll has proven very effective in all chronic disorders. Scientific experiments have shown that its structure is almost identical to that of hemoglobin. It differs only in some peripheral molecules and in the central atom.

"His flesh shall be fresh as a child's; he shall return, to the days, of his youth.
— Job 33:25

Chlorophyll can regenerate the bloodstream. In animal and clinical studies it has proven effective in overcoming most forms of anemia (a hemoglobin deficiency). Hence, in the human body, chlorophyll can be used interchangeably with hemoglobin.

Other studies have shown chlorophyll in live food to greatly increase survival of those exposed to lethal radiation. City dwellers are daily exposed to radiation from strontium 90, iodine 131, fluorescent lights, x-rays, radioactive pollutants. Chlorophyll-rich grass juice is a very protective drink.

Grass juice can dissolve the scars that are formed in the lungs from breathing acid gasses. The effect of carbon monoxide is minimized, since chlorophyll increases hemoglobin production.

A live food diet decreases the food requirement, hence the bloodstream will not be congested with incompletely metabolised food, toxins or waste products of metabolism. As a result, the eliminative organs can more efficiently deal with inhaled air pollutants.

Vik — 1972

Grass for breathing and not for smoking

"For the power of God's angels enters into you with the living food which the Lord gives you from his royal table. And when you eat, have above you the angel of air, and below you the angel of water. Breathe long and deeply at all your meals, that the angel of air may bless your repasts. And chew well your food with your teeth, that it become water, and that the angel of water turn it into blood in your body. And eat slowly, as it were a prayer you make to the Lord. For I tell you truly, the power of God enters into you, if you eat after this manner at his table."

—The Essene Gospel of Peace,
Prof. Edmond Szekely

recipes

Each one of these recipes should be thought of as a complete meal. Benjamin Franklin said, "Many dishes, many diseases." When serving two recipes at the same time, follow the food combining chart.

Easy to Digest — If in doubt whether a recipe is digestible for you, simplify it, or eat it alone, on an empty stomach, and in small quantity.

In this book there are some transitional recipes which combine fruits and vegetables, as well as acid and sweet fruit (such as citrus and super-ripe banana). These recipes should be avoided if you have digestive problems. Most individuals can handle and obtain benefit from such meals. Likewise, avocado, coconut butter and oil when overblended, can be hard on the digestion. Those on therapy programs should omit fats from their diet. All fats slow the digestive process, are not necessary to the diet and should be used (if ever) in moderation. Choose only raw virgin-press oils or avocado.

breakfast

"The ancient Greeks, before the time of Lycurgus, ate nothing but fruit." (Plutarch) and, "each generation reached the age of 200 years."

— Onomacritus of Athens

Eat fruit at room temperature.

IDEAL BREAKFAST

Your choice of fruit.

If available, have organic citrus fruit. Or banana and apple; mango and avocado; two papaya. This type of breakfast is ideal during the warm part of the year.

AMBROSIA

½ avocado
8 pitted dates or
2 slices pineapple (dried or fresh)

½ cup water

Blend. Add more water if desired. Very sweet.

SUN KISSED ENERGY

½ cup raisins   2 cups water
4 halves dried apricots

Soak the ingredients for a day at room temperature and for another day in the refrigerator, or until its former roundness returns, perhaps up to four days. The same applies to dried cherries, apricots, apples, figs and prunes.

BROWN BROTHERHOOD SOUP

9 dried figs   1 cup warm water

Blend until smooth. A delicious meal.

"Living is actually a struggle for fresh air, keep the vast lung surface of the organism supplied with fresh, unpolluted air, and also observe all the other health rules, and there is no reason known to science why you should ever die."

— Prof. J.S. Haldane, English Astronomer

MELON FRAPPE

½ ripe melon, diced

Blend until smooth.

PRUNEDATE

5 pitted dates   1 or 2 ripe bananas
½ cup cold water   3 large pitted prunes

Blend fruit and cold water to a smooth consistency. Add a quarter cup of hot water. Serve over sliced bananas.

TROPICAL FRUIT SOUP

10-12 oz. mango, papaya,   1-2 tbs. avocado
     pineapple, strawberries   water if needed
1 tbs. citrus juice

Blend until smooth.

drinks

Any of the drinks make a good breakfast.

LIMEADE

| Juice of 1 lime (or lemon) | 2 cups warm water |
| honey or molasses (optional) | 1 crushed mint leaf (optional) |

This is the morning drink at the Institute. If food from the previous night has not been completely digested, grogginess, headache, burning eyes or nausea may result. Wait until you feel hungry to have this drink. If you must have it sooner, avoid sweeteners and drink only half a cup. Sweets help to further fermentation of food still present in the stomach. This is highly undesirable. If possible, skip the water and have organic citrus fruit.

RISING SUN

| 2 oz. wheatgrass juice | 6 oz. pure water (or rejuvelac) |

Dilute juice in water and drink on an empty stomach. People with health problems should drink this 3 times daily. If at first the juice disagrees with you, use smaller portions. Even 1 tablespoon of juice or just chewing the grass is beneficial. As you become more used to it, your body will be able to take it in larger quantity. It tastes much like ordinary grass but is sweeter. King Nebuchadnezzar by "eating grass as did the oxen" became well.

SOLARIZER

| 1 oz. wheatgrass juice | 3 oz. organic carrot juice |

Mix the juices. This is an excellent drink for a child. Give him a healthy start in the morning.

CHLOROPHYLL COCKTAIL

1 oz. wheatgrass juice   **1 oz. barley grass juice**
6 oz. water

Wheat is very sweet, barley is bitter. The mixture, diluted with water, makes a tasty drink, the two flavors complement each other. If barley is not available, ½ oz. dandelion juice can be used as a substitute.

CHLOROPHYLL IMPLANT

4-8 oz. wheatgrass juice

First take one quart warm water enema. Expel the water. Follow by grass juice enema. Afterward, lie at least 20 minutes on slant board with feet elevated. The nutrients will be absorbed into your bloodstream. This will aid digestion and help to alleviate constipation. It is effective in removing worms.

NORTHERN FOUNTAIN OF YOUTH

4 parts carrot juice   **2 parts beet juice**
4 parts celery juice   **1 part wheatgrass juice**

Mix the juices and sip slowly. Season with a dash of mint and kelp powder.

GRASS HELP

1 oz. wheatgrass juice   **7 oz. distilled water**
½ tsp. kelp

Soak kelp for 5 minutes in 2 oz. hot distilled water. Strain. Add the cold water. Add grass juice and drink.

WHEAT CIDER

Begin as for rejuvelac recipe (above) but let wheat seed soak in water for 4 days. Drink the fluid or use it as a basis for preparation of chick pea, soybean, or sesame sauces.

"Do not follow the footsteps of the ancients, seek what they sought."

— Basho

REJUVELAC

1 cup wheat   **2 cups water**

Wash wheat and soak in water for 24 hours. Pour water into another container. Let soak water stand at room temperature for at least 1 day. It will taste somewhat like whey. Use it alone or for blending foods. When properly prepared, this drink provides an inexpensive source of friendly bacteria, which are a necessary component of healthy intestinal flora. (Use the soaked seed to grow grass).

A much stronger sour drink, which at times tastes like sauerkraut or lemon or exotic wine, can be created by allowing the wheat to continue to soak under refrigeration. Each time you pour off a drink, refill the container to the previous level. It may be kept for weeks to give you a delightful drink. The liquid, when blended with ground sesame and kelp, makes a delicious dressing for salads.

WATERMELON

Let watermelon reach room temperature. Blend chunks of watermelon (may include seed). Begin by blending a small amount. Add the rest slowly. When liquefied, strain through cheesecloth or fine strainer. Drink as frequently as desired (no more than 2 cups per serving), preferably on an empty stomach. A very soothing drink for over-acidity of the body. A watermelon fast is an effective way of losing weight, ideal for cleansing kidneys and liver. Instead of blending, chew the watermelon and spit out the pulp, or squeeze the juice out through a stainless steel strainer by crushing the watermelon with a fork.

SUNSHINE

1 banana   **1 cup papaya, diced**
1 cup apple juice
Blend until smooth.

VITAMINS FOR THIRD EYE

1 papaya, diced   **2 oranges, juiced**
Blend papaya and juice to a puree. A very good aid to digestion.

MILK OF EDEN

1 cup coconut, chopped   **1 cup water**

At high speed, blend coconut and water to creamy consistency. Strain through a fine sieve.

BANANA FLOAT

1 cup ripe, sweet orange juice   **1 ripe banana**

Blend at low speed.

DARK BANANA

1 ripe banana   **4 pitted dates**
1 cup water

Blend dates and water to smooth consistency. Blend in banana.

EVE'S NECTAR

1 ripe banana   **few drops oil**
1 cup seedless grapes

Blend.

GRAPED AVOCADO

1 cup seedless grapes   **mint leaves (optional)**
½ avocado

Blend. If too thick, add more grapes.

SWEET OM TUM

3 ripe apples, medium   **few drops oil**
1 cup seedless grapes

Blend.

SHAKESPEARE

1 ripe banana   1 spearmint leaf
1 cup coconut milk (or rejuvelac)

Blend all ingredients.

BANANA DELIGHT

1 ripe banana   ½ cup rejuvelac
½ avocado   mint leaves (optional)

Blend.

KORAL KISS

1 cup ripe tomato   few drops oil
1 ripe banana

Blend.

TROPIC DREAM

1 ripe banana   ½ cup comfrey tea
¼ cup coconut butter

Blend.

FLAXATIVE

¼ cup flax seed   1 cup warm water
1 banana

Soak seed overnight. Blend all ingredients. Has laxative effect.

ALL-NIGHTER

2 oz. parsley juice   8 oz. water

Stir together, A very powerful juice; use in moderation.

GREEN SUNSHINE

1 oz. wheatgrass juice	3 mint leaves
1 handful sorrel	6 oz. water
6 dandelion leaves	

With wheatgrass juicer extract juice from leaves. Choose type and amount of greens to suit your taste: wheat is sweet, dandelion is bitter; sorrel is lemonish; mint adds fragrance.

CUCUMBER COOL

2 unpeeled fresh cucumbers	lemon or lime juice

Blend cucumbers. Season with citrus. Tasty variations can be made with orange or grapefruit juice or by blending in ¼ avocado. The high alkaline mineral content of this drink can be a great aid in clearing up skin ailments.

V-8

2 tomatoes	2 carrots
1 sweet pepper	1 stalk celery
1 cucumber	½ tsp. kelp
3 sprigs parsley	

Juice vegetables. Season to taste. As a nutritional booster, mix in several tablespoons of wheatgrass juice just before serving. Very tasty — contains all the essential vitamins and minerals.

ALFEE

½ pound alfalfa sprouts

Let the alfalfa grow for a week or more in glass sprouting jars. At all times keep it exposed to light. Juice with a Health Fountain juicer. Dilute with water if the flavor is too strong. If you cannot plant wheatgrass, sprouting alfalfa and wheat for 7 days provides an excellent substitute. The green leaves make an excellent chlorophyl drink.

REAL CHOCOLATE

8 oz. carrot juice	1 oz. dandelion juice
2 oz. beet juice	

Mix. Strong bloodbuilder. Tastes like chocolate.

fruit salads

These fruit salads should be eaten alone. Fine for lunch or supper.

ARABIAN APPLE

2 diced apples
1/3 cup rejuvelac

1/3 cup almond meal
1 tsp. kelp

Mix or blend rejuvelac, kelp and ground almonds. Pour over apples.

ACID TRIP

2 cups ripe tomato, cubed
1 cup ripe pineapple, diced

1 tbs. oil (optional)

Mix ingredients and serve.

AUTUMN

2 cups raspberries

¼ cup sesame meal

Wash berries and sprinkle with sesame meal.

BLUE MOON

2 cups blueberries
1 peeled apple, diced

1 cup grapes
1 avocado, diced

Mix ingredients. Toss with a fork. Add mangos or pitted cherries when available. Eat plain or serve with skylight sauce.

FRUIT AND NUTS

½ cup ripe banana
¼ cup papaya

¼ cup sunflower seed
meal or whole sunflower
sprouts

Serve fruit diced, sprinkled with sunflower seed meal or 1 day sprouted sunflower.

LATE SUMMER

1 apple, diced

2 peaches, diced

1 cup grapes

1 pear, sliced

1 banana, sliced

Mix ingredients. Serve plain or season with kelp and oil.

MELON PERSIANALTY

I part watermelon

3 parts Persian melon

3 parts honeydew

3 parts canteloupe

Cut into all kinds of shapes — balls, cubes, strips of varying thickness and arrange. It is very important to eat this meal on an empty stomach.

"And thy youth shall be renewed like the eagle.

— Ps. 103:5

ROAD TO EDEN

1 papaya   1 mango   1 avocado

Slice fruit in long thin strips. Interlace and serve on bed of iceburg lettuce. May serve with avocado strip dressing.

NUTS AMONG THE BERRIES

1 cup raspberries

½ cup water

¼ cup almond meal

Pick berries in season. Blend almonds and water to a cream to pour over berries. Each month produces its own berries, they are a most desirable breakfast food.

SESAME FRUIT

1 ripe apple

1 cup sesame meal

1 ripe banana

cinnamon

Dice banana and apple and pour sesame on top, thoroughly covering fruit. Sprinkle lightly with cinnamon.

SUN KISSED

1 cup raisins

¼ cup dried prunes

¼ cup dried peaches

1 cup dried apricots

½ avocado

Wash fruit, cover with water. Soak at room temperature for 24 hours. Place in refrigerator to prevent fermentation and leave there for at least 2 days, until fruits fill out to their natural shapes. Serve plain or with a sauce made from their juice blended with avocado. Most fruits that can be dried are fully ripened on the tree. As a result, their sugar content can be as much as 30% higher than that of the same fruits eaten fresh. This makes them an excellent source of food during the winter, when an abundant supply of native fruit is not available. Dried fruit is a concentrated food, since it takes 5½ pounds of apricots or 3½ pounds of grapes to make one pound of dried fruit. It should not be eaten in abundance since it will cause the teeth to deteriorate because of its high sugar content (especially dates or figs.)

WATERY APPLE SALAD

2 large tomatoes, wedged

1 cup ripe sweet pineapple, diced

1 sour apple, diced

2 cups Romaine lettuce

Toss salad. Use no dressing.

"Seek the fresh air of the forest and of the fields, and there in the midst of them shall you find the angel of air. Put off your shoes and your clothing and suffer the angel of air to embrace all your body. Then breathe long and deeply, that the angel of air may be brought within you. I tell you truly, the angel of air shall cast out of your body all uncleannesses which defiled it without and within. And thus shall all evil-smelling and unclean things rise out of you, as the smoke of fire curls upwards and is lost in the sea of the air. For I tell you truly, holy is the angel of air, who cleanses all that is unclean and makes all evil-smelling things of a sweet odour. No man may come before the face of God, whom the angel of air lets not pass. Truly, all must be born again by air and by truth, for your body breathes the air of the Earthly Mother, and your spirit breathes the truth of the Heavenly Father."

—The Essene Gospel of Peace,
Prof. Edmond Szekely

The press of May 3rd, 1936 reported the case of Srimati Giri Bala Devi of Patrasayar in Bankura, India, who had taken neither food nor water for 56 years: "She takes nothing, not even a drop of water. She is always gay and looks like a child. She does not pass stool nor urine, and does her house work like any other woman."

— Man's Higher Consciousness

little chew fruit salad

YELLOW-GREEN

1 ripe avocado   **1 ripe mango**

Peel fruit and cut into bite-size pieces. Combine and serve. Very good for introducing avocado to those who are not familiar with it.

APPLE SAUCE

2 large apples, diced   **¼ cup apple (orange)**
¼ cup raisins   **juice**
2 tsp. lemon juice

Blend raisins with juice. Blend apples.

APPLE AMBROSIA

2 apples   **¼ cup orange juice**
¼ cup pecans

Blend until smooth.

BANANA NUT

1 banana   **1 tbs. water**
2 tbs. almond butter

Dilute almond butter with water. Pour over sliced banana.

"I am your animal nature, if you would pass on to the higher life, then me you must master."

— Gen. 2:17, Cor. 7:1

earthy salads

Many of these salads are a complete meal. If they contain seeds or nuts do not combine them with starches. Use oil OR avocado, OR seed. Leafy greens and cabbage aid in digestion of fat and protein. Adjust amount of ingredients to your needs.

ALFALFA HAWAIIAN

1 cup alfalfa sprouts	½ cup sesame sprouts
1 cup diced pineapple	¼ cup sesame meal

Blend pineapple to desired consistency. Pour over salad mixture.

SALAD ROLL

1 tomato, wedged	¼ cup sesame or
lettuce leaves, large	sunflower meal

Place tomato on lettuce leaves. Sprinkle with seed meal. May roll lettuce leaves tightly around other ingredients and eat with fingers.

SHILOH

1 head lettuce	1 bell pepper, cut fine
1 cup shredded red cabbage	1 avocado, diced
1 large tomato, diced fine	1 tsp. kelp
½ cup mung sprouts	

Tear lettuce into bite-size pieces. Much tastier than when cut with a knife. Toss salad and serve.

SIESTA SALAD

1 cup chopped tomato	1 cup mung sprouts
½ cup sliced celery	½ cup red onion rings
¼ cup chopped green pepper	(optional)
3 cups shredded lettuce	

Toss lightly and serve with Mexican salad dressing.

GENESIS 1:29 DIET

"And God Said, 'See, I give you every plant that bears seed all over the earth, and every tree with seed in its fruit; be that your food'."

ALFIE SALAD

2 cups alfalfa sprouts
5 radishes, sliced,
   or radish sprouts
3 tomatoes, wedged
3 tbs. spanish onion, diced

2 cups shredded
   Romaine lettuce
1 large green pepper,
   sliced in rings

Toss salad. Serve with one of the sauces as a side dish, or add your favorite dressing.

ALMOND SLAW

¼ med. cabbage
¼ cup almond meal

pinch dill leaves
dash kelp

Grate cabbage fine. Mix with almond meal and seasoning. May add mung sprouts.

PRAISE ALFIE

1 cup alfalfa sprouts
2 carrots, grated fine

1 cup minced celery

Toss salad. Serve with firebird dressing.

AQUARIAN SALAD

1 cup carrots, grated fine
1 cup cabbage, grated fine
1 cup diced celery
1 red sour apple, diced fine

1 cup sprouted alfalfa
4 tbs. pineapple juice
1 tbs. kelp

Toss salad and serve.

AUTUMN SYMPHONY

2 cups red cabbage, shredded
3 stalks celery, graded
1 cup carrot, grated

1 green pepper cut in rings
¼ cup apples
4 tbs. red onion, diced fine
(optional)

Mix celery, cabbage, carrots and apples. Sprinkle with onion and cover with pepper rings. Serve with Rising Sun dressing.

BEET TREET

4 beet leaves, cut fine
1 stalk celery, minced
1 cup cabbage, shredded
1 small beet, grated fine

¼ cup mung sprouts
parsley and mint leaves,
minced
½ avocado, mashed

Mix ingredients. Season with kelp if desired.

COLE SLAW

2 cups shredded cabbage
1 cup shredded turnips

1 cup shredded carrots

Mix ingredients. Moisten thoroughly with sesonnaise or sunset or cole slaw dressing.

CUMIN LETTUCE

½ head loose leaf lettuce
2 tbs. olive oil

pinch ground cumin
dash kelp

Tear lettuce into bite-size pieces. Season.

ENZYME SALAD

2 cups sprouts
1 cup chopped greens
¼ cup wheatgrass,
chopped fine

2 tbs. oil
2 tsp. kelp
juice of ½ lemon

Choose greens from among the following: spinach, watercress, brussels sprouts, beet, celery or dandelion. Mix all ingredients and season.

DILL CABBAGE

¼ med. cabbage
2 tbs. olive oil

pinch dill leaves
dash kelp

Grate cabbage fine. Mix with seasoning. May add mung sprouts.

HOT HADES

1 small spanish onion, diced
1 small hot pepper,
   diced fine
1 celery stalk, diced

2 large tomatoes, wedged
½ avocado, diced

Very hot, spicy — not for people with delicate digestive systems — should not be used except during the transition period from ordinary food to live food. Toss salad. Serve with Mexican dressing.

GENESIS SALAD

1 cup sorrel
1 cup comfrey, rolled tight
   and cut fine
3 nasturtium leaves, cut very
   fine
½ cup rose petals
1 handful chives, cut fine

1 cup lambsquarters,
   cut fine
4 dandelion leaves,
   cut fine
3 peppermint leaves,
   crushed
1 tbs. sea kelp (optional)
2 tbs. oil (optional)

Toss salad. Make sure there is plenty of color on surface of salad. Add nasturtium leaves. As you eat, think of the following Biblical quotation: "I have given you every herb bearing seed, which is upon the face of all the earth, and every tree, in which is the fruit of a tree yielding seed; to you it shall be for meat." Genesis (I, 29)

GERMINATED SALAD

1 cup sprouts
1 cup shredded carrots
1 handful watercress

3 cubed tomatoes
1 cup chopped celery
½ cup chopped dulse
   leaves

Soak dulse in ¼ cup water. Toss salad — serve with pineapple dressing.

GRATED TUBERS

Choose from any array of available tubers: beets, peeled rutabaga, parsnip, beans in jackets and all squashes. They are all storehouses of sugar and become highly digestible and tasty when grated, shredded or blended with a little water. Before preparing, scrub tubers with vegetable brush. Use sesonnaise as a side dish. Decorate it with tasty squash flowers.

INDOOR FARM SALAD

3 cups six day alfalfa sprouts
½ cup four day radish sprouts
½ cup three day mung sprouts
½ cup three day fenugreek sprouts
1 cup six day buckwheat lettuce

1 cup six day sunflower
    greens
½ cup sesame meal
1 lime (optional)
2 tbs. kelp

Remove any shells still present on sunflower and buckwheat greens. Cut them up fine. Toss salad and season to taste.

LIVE GERMS

1 cup favorite germinated seed
2 cups shredded lettuce or cabbage

Toss salad. Serve with or without dressing.

LOVE APPLE

3 large ripe tomatoes, diced   1 head Romaine lettuce

Tear lettuce into bite-size pieces. Toss salad and serve with an abundant supply of enzyme trip or vatican dressing.

NASTURTIUM MEAL

1 cup nasturtium leaves
1 cup purslane

½ cup dandelion leaves
1 cup grated carrots

Cut up greens. Serve with avocado strip dressing.

NORTHERN

3 med. tomatoes, diced
2 green peppers, sliced
1 avocado, cubed

1 med. cucumber, in
season, diced

Mix ingredients. Use fork to break up avocado. Eat plain or season with kelp and herbs.

MUNG SALAD

1 cup mung sprouts
½ cup sprouted sesame
¼ cup ground sesame (optional)

½ cup buckwheat
lettuce
1 tsp. kelp

Mix ingredients and serve. Rejuvelac may be added for moisture.

NATURE'S SALAD

½ cup grass, cut fine
½ cup nasturtium leaves, flowers

1 cup rose petals
1 cup favorite weeds

Toss salad. Serve with favorite dressing. Chew thoroughly.

SIMPLE SALAD

2 cups mung sprouts
2 tbs. oil or
¼ cup seed meal

dash kelp or
chopped dulse

A complete meal. Can be eaten every day.

SPROUT SALAD

2 cups alfalfa
½ cup lentil
½ cup wheatgrass, cut fine

1 cup mung
1 cup ground chick pea
2 tbs. chives, chopped
fine

Toss salad. Serve with your favorite oil and dash of kelp.

Dr. Robert McCarrison, M.D., British Army Medical Service Himalayan region said: "Men well over 200 years of age were working in the fields with much younger men, doing as much work, and looked so much like the younger men, that it was unable to distinguish the old from the young."

— K.L. Coe, Correct Eating and Strength, Mr 1931.

UNDERGROUND SALAD

1 cup grated carrots
½ cup grated parsnips
2 Jerusalem artichokes, sliced thin

¼ cup grated beets
4 red radishes, sliced
   thin

Toss Salad. Serve on bed of lettuce with avocado strip dressing.

VEGEFRUIT

1 diced carrot
1 cup buckwheat lettuce
1 cup chopped celery

½ diced avocado
1 cup grated apple

Mix ingredients and serve.

VOLCANIC GREEN

1 cup diced, ripe pineapple
½ diced avocado
2 cups iceburg lettuce

1 green bell pepper
2 tomatoes, wedged
1 tsp. kelp

Blend or toss pineapple, half a pepper and kelp with small amount of water. Dice other half of pepper. Tear lettuce into bite-size pieces. Toss salad ingredients. Serve in bowl with blended sauce.

YOUTH SALAD

1 head romaine lettuce
½ cup ground sesame seed

1 cup favorite sprouts
juice 1 lemon

Wash and drain lettuce, tear into small pieces. Add sprouts, sesame and lemon. Toss salad. For variation, substitute home-grown buckwheat lettuce or sunflower greens for romaine.

RED CURRANT

½ cup sour red currants
1 cucumber sliced thin
½ cup avocado, diced

2 diced tomatoes
½ head Romaine lettuce

Toss salad. Serve plain or with Firebird dressing.

"Appetite comes with eating."

— F.A. Ridley

little chew

ALFALFA GREEN

½ cup avocado
½ cup carrot juice

1 small yellow squash
½ cup alfalfa sprouts

Blend squash and carrot juice. Serve over alfalfa sprouts and diced avocado. Serve plain or season with lime and/or kelp.

ALVICUTO

1 avocado, diced
1 med. fresh cucumber, diced

1 large tomato
1 lime

Blend cucumber to creamy consistency. Add lime and tomato at slow speed, partially blending in tomato. Serve over avocado. Add your favorite seasoning if desired. Cucumbers should be young and crisp. If waxed or old, remove skin.

AVOCADO PUDDING

1 avocado
1 cup rejuvelac

dash onion
dash lemon juice

Blend until smooth.

SHREDDED SALAD

1 cup carrots, grated fine
1 cup shredded Romaine
   lettuce
½ avocado

¼ cup grated beets
1 cup alfalfa sprouts
1 tsp. kelp

Blend thoroughly at slow speed in a small amount of water, sprouts and kelp. Pour into bowl and mix with diced avocado. Toss remaining ingredients, add sauce and serve.

sauces

Any of these sauces served over mung or alfalfa sprouts make a complete meal.

rainbow protein sauces

Food contains trapped solar vibrations which are made visible by the predominant colors. The harmony of food is indicated by its color. Beautiful, bright, rainbow colors make you happy, vibrant and healthy. Brown, black and other dark colors depress and lower vitality. Sun gives the most perfect blend of colors, which result in the purity of the white.

Sunbathing eliminates the desire for food. Excess of sun creates the same effect as excess of food. When receiving the solar energy, via food mixtures, be sure that the effect of combination does not create a color black, brown or gray. This is the color of cooked food. They bring on disharmony and death. They drain your vitality. Simplest meals with a predominant color are best.

"Man eats solar vibrations trapped in nutrients. Enzymes, protein, vitamins are temporary energy traps, under the action of enzymes these energies are released for building and maintenance of the human body. Some individuals get the needed nutrients via sun and color, most via food."

— Survival Into 21st Century

SESSONAISE — WHITE

1 cup sesame meal   ½ lime
1 cup water   1 tbs. kelp

Pour water into blender. Blend in sesame (or sunflower, almond, pecan) meal at high speed. Reduce to creamy consistency. Add lime juice. Add seasoning (do not drop into vortex for this would make it difficult to blend with other ingredients). Makes 2 cups.

ENZYME TRIP — PALE GREEN

1 cup sprounted soybeans   1 very small onion
½ cup celery leaves   ½ cup rejuvelac
½ avocado   tsp. kelp

Blend rejuvelac and sprouts to creamy consistency. Add avocado and season to taste. Makes 2 cups.

INDOOR SAUCE — GREEN

2 cups buckwheat greens   ½ cup sesame meal
½ cup sunflower greens   1 cup rejuvelac
5 large comfrey leaves   kelp to taste

Blend sesame and rejuvelac to cream. Blend in other ingredients. Serve over sprouts. Makes 3 cups.

ORIENTAL — SUNSET GOLD

1 cup sprouted soybeans   1 cup rejuvelac
1 large stalk celery, chopped   ¼ cup safflower oil
3 med. carrots, shredded   2 tbs. kelp

Blend sprouts with rejuvelac. Initially use low speed, then reduce to creamy consistency on high speed. Add oil. Blend in carrots and then celery, a little at a time. Add seasoning. Makes 3 cups.

RUSSIAN SPIRIT — RED

¼ cup soy sprouts   ½ cup rejuvelac
1 large red pepper   ¼ cup safflower oil
2 limes   2 tsp. kelp

Blend sprouts and rejuvelac to creamy consistency at high speed. Add oil and lime juice. Blend in pepper. Season to taste with kelp. Serve over romaine and tomato salad. Reminiscent of Russian dressing. Makes 2 cups.

vegetable rainbow sauces

Rainbow sauces may be used as salad dressings if used in proper combination.

BEET FREAK — DARK RED

1 med. beet, diced	1 cup water
¼ avocado or 2 tbs. oil	1 tsp kelp

Blend beets and water a little at a time until liquefied. Add avocado and seasoning. Makes 1½ cups.

CARAWAY BEETS — PURPLE

2 small beets, diced	2 tbs oil
1 small red pepper	¼ cup water
1 stalk celery	1 tsp kelp
½ tsp caraway seed,	
soaked overnight (optional)	
lemon or lime	

Pour water and oil into blender. Using high speed, blend in beets a little at a time. Add celery and pepper — liquify. Add lime juice and seasonings. The taste of beet should not be strong. If too pronounced add more lime juice. The finished sauce should have the flavor of pickled beets. Use as a dressing for leafy greens.

COMFREY SAUCE — DEEP GREEN

comfrey leaves	2 tbs. oil
buckwheat lettuce	kelp to taste
rejuvelac	

Blend and serve over sprouts or leafy green salad.

DEEP WINTER — GOLD

1 cup diced butternut squash	¼ cup water
¼ avocado	1 tsp kelp

Blend squash and thicken with avocado. Season to taste. Makes 1 cup.

ZUCCHINI GREEN SOUP

2 cups Zucchini
1 cup buckwheat greens
1 cup rejuvelac

2 tbs. oil (optional)
kelp to taste
garlic, clove (optional)

Blend. Serve over mung sprouts and dulse leaves. Very healing, blood cleansing.

GREEN SAUCE

2 cups indoor salad greens
1 cup water
onion to taste
seasoning (kelp, dulse, herbs)

½ avocado OR
1 tbs oil OR
¼ cup sesame or sunflower meal

Blend greens, water, seasoning. For thickening, blend in avocado or oil or seed (only one of these). A good cold soup or dressing.

OKRA ROCK — GREEN

½ cup fresh okra
1 cup tomato
¼ avocado

2 oz lime juice
1 tbs kelp

Blend okra and tomato. Add lime juice. Thicken with avocado. Season. Makes 2 cups.

CARBEET — PINK

1 small beet
1 small carrot
2 oz. lime juice (optional)

¼ cup oil
¼ cup water
2 tbs kelp

Scrub and dice vegetables. Pour liquids into blender. Blend in tubers at high speed, a little at a time. Continue blending to creamy consistency. Season to taste.

NORTHERN FRUIT — RED

2 ripe tomatoes
1 carrot
1 stalk celery

2 peppers
¼ avocado
sprig parsley, mint, sorrel

Blend tomato, followed by carrot. If more fluid is needed, add carrot juice. Blend in pepper and celery. Add avocado as thickener. Season with herbs. Makes 1½ cups.

VISIONS OF GOLD — ORANGE

2 cups chopped yellow
  squash
½ cup water

¼ cup oil
1 tsp kelp
2 cups chopped carrots

Place water and oil into blender and blend in carrots at low speed. If this is difficult, turn blender rapidly on and off to aid the creaming process. Add squash and blend. Season to taste. For variation, replace oil with avocado and/or water with carrot juice. Makes 2½ cups.

SMILING FLOWER — SILENT GREEN

½ cup diced carrots
½ cup water

½ avocado
1 tsp kelp

Blend carrots with a little water, using the on/off technique. Add avocado, and more water if needed. Season and serve over sprouts or mixed with sprouts as a sandwich filler. Makes 1 cup.

THANKSGIVING — YELLOW

1 cup sweet corn
½ cup water

¼ cup safflower oil
2 tbs kelp

Pour water and oil into blender. Blend in corn to creamy consistency. Add kelp. For variation, try mixing in finely diced red pepper. Makes 2 cups.

TURNED-ON-SQUASH — DEEP YELLOW

1 cup diced yellow squash
1 cup diced turnip

½ avocado
¼ cup water

Blend squash and turnip (or parsnips), followed by avocado. Add water as needed. If desired, season with kelp, mint or herbs.

GREEN LOVE

½ cup zucchini
handful buckwheat lettuce
¾ cup alfalfa sprouts
¼ cup mung sprouts

½ cup rejuvelac
1/6 avocado OR
¼ cup sesame OR
  sunflower meal
dash kelp (optional)

Blend seed or avocado with rejuvelac. Blend in other ingredients.

VICHYSOISSE VERDE — DEEP GREEN

2 cups chopped greens   ½ avocado
1 cup water   1 tsp kelp
optional - choose one: 3 mint leaves,
½ clove garlic, juice 1 lemon,
1 small onion, 3 scallion leaves

Use two or more varieties of greens in season: swiss chard and spinach; beets tops and celery; lettuce and celery are tasty combinations. Pour water in blender. Add greens at slow speed a little at a time. Reduce to a fine consistency. Add more greens if sauce is very thin. Blend in one optional ingredient to taste. Blend in avocado. Serve immediately as a dressing on salad or sprouts, or as a soup. Makes 3 cups.

"The sun gives all things life and fertility. It is the true god of the earth."
— Napoleon

Seven day dance of sunflower greens. Performed under the direction of God, in the home of Viktoras —

LOVE

"Though I speak with the tongues of men and of angels, but have not love, I am sounding brass or a tinkling cymbal. Though I tell what is to come, and know all secrets, and all wisdom; and though I have faith strong as the storm which lifts mountains from their seat, but have not love, I am nothing. And though I bestow all my goods to feed the poor, and give all my fire that I have received from my Father, but have not love, I am in no wise profited. Love is patient, love is kind. Love is not envious, works not evil, knows not pride; is not rude, neither selfish; is slow to anger, imagines no mischief; rejoices not in injustice, but delights in justice. Love defends all, love believes all, love hopes all, love bears all; never exhausts itself; but as for tongues they shall cease, and, as for knowledge, it shall vanish away."

—The Essene Gospel of Peace,
Prof. Edmond Szekely

"Others will never be able to love you as you want to be loved until you are willing to communicate yourself to them completely -- getting them to understand your barriers (what stands between you and them), your fears (what you think will be the consequences of your honesty: rejection, loneliness, ridicule, torture, death...). Through slowly developing the confidence that others can accept and understand you, you can begin to present yourself to them, as you really are, without disguises. You can tell them more of what you really think about things, more about what you want from them, what you're like, what you feel. As you learn to trust your ability to get yourself across to those closest to you, you realize that you have the ability to present yourself to anyone you wish."

"Games have nothing to do with love, except to demonstrate that you are afraid of losing something, of being hurt and betrayed. But you cannot lose in love, because love is not a game. Love is in the little things -- the smallest gesture of another is a love poem, if you learn how to read it. See others from their viewpoint: what does what they do mean to them, what are they telling you about themselves by the way they hold their body, the way they look at you, how they dress, how they hesitate or rush about. Learn how to understand their silences. And learn how to differentiate your thoughts, emotions, and states of being from theirs. And be patient."

"Let it happen. Love will be there when you stop trying to create an effect. Letting go of your ego means only that you stop caring what you think the other thinks of you, and just relate to him as you know you are. Let it happen. You'll be loved by everyone when you decide to love all of them, when you commit yourself to fulfilling your end of your love affair with all others. Open your heart and mind to the infinite excitement of your relationship to every living being. You'll discover that you and everyone else would give anything to experience the pure love that relates us all. And the only thing there is to give is yourself."

—Jeff Linzer

"It is by love that the Heavenly Father and the Earthly Mother and the Son of Man become one. For the spirit of the Son of Man was created from the spirit of the Heavenly Father, and his body from the body of the Earthly Mother."

—The Essene Gospel of Peace,
Prof. Edmond Szekely

47

fruit rainbow sauces

Use the fruit sauces alone or properly combined with fruit.

FRUIT-SEED SAUCE

7-8 oz fresh citrus fruit
2-3 tbs soaked seed or nuts

1 tbs lemon or lime juice
water as needed

Chop fruit. Blend all ingredients until texture is pleasing.

FRUIT-COCONUT SAUCE

7-8 oz fresh citrus fruit
2-5 tbs grated coconut

1 tbs lemon or lime juice
water as needed.

Chop fruit. Blend all ingredients until texture is pleasing.

MEDITERRANEAN — WHITE

1 ripe banana
½ avocado
½ cup water

1 tsp kelp
¼ tsp ginger root
(optional)

Blend banana with water. Add lime, avocado and kelp. If necessary, thin with water. Serve on tropical sweet or subacid salads. For variation: substitute ¼ cup oil for avocado. Makes 1 cup.

SKYLIGHT — BLUE

1 cup blueberries
1 ripe banana

1 lime
¼ cup water

Blend berries, adding water as needed. At low speed, work in the banana and lime. Serve over a subacid fruit salad. Makes 1 cup.

salad dressings

AVOCADO STRIP

½ avocado   1 tsp. kelp
1 oz. lime juice

Blend avocado to creamy consistency, using fork or blender. Season to taste and serve over fruit or green salad. Makes 1/2 cup.

VATICAN

3 oz. olive oil   1 oz. lemon juice
3 natural olives

Blend ingredients. Serve over salad of lettuce, pepper, tomato. Makes 1/2 cup.

SUNSET

2 tbs. safflower oil   2 tbs. lemon juice
6 tbs. beet juice   1 tsp. honey

Blend ingredients until foamy. Makes 1/2 cup.

FIREBIRD

½ cup olive oil   4 tbs. lime juice
¼ cup tomato juice or pulp   1 tbs. kelp

Blend all ingredients until foamy. Makes 1 cup.

MEXICAN

3 oz. olive oil   1 oz. lime juice
1 clove garlic   1 tbs. kelp

Mash garlic with fork against side of cup containing oil. Remove pulp. Add remaining ingredients, shake thoroughly. Serve over leafy salad. Makes 1/2 cup.

CARROT CRUSH

½ cup diced raw carrots   1 tbs. kelp
¼ cup safflower oil

Blend ingredients to fine consistency. Makes 1/2 cup.

RISING SUN

4 oz. safflower oil   1 tsp. kelp
2 oz. lime juice

Blend with fork. Shake well before using. Makes 1/2 cup.

GREEN CHEESE

½ cup chick pea sprouts   rejuvelac
¼ avocado   2 tsp. kelp

Blend sprouts with water. Add avocado and seasoning. Very appetizing over sprouted chick peas or leafy greens. Makes 2 cups.

TOMATO-PEPPER

2-3 ripe tomatoes   water as needed
1 med. red pepper   1 tbs. kelp
2 tbs. oil   lime juice

Blend tomatoes, pepper, oil, water until smooth. Season to taste.

"It is better to do nothing, than to waste time."

—Viktoras

fruit salad dressings

APPLE

2 oz. olive oil **1 oz. lemon juice**
2 oz. apple juice (or sauce)

Mix and serve over a green salad. Makes 1/2 cup.

BACK TO EDEN

2 cups strawberries or blueberries **3 lemons, juiced**
1 grapefruit, juiced **4 oranges, juiced**
¼ tsp. ginger root

Blend berries. Pour in citrus juice and ginger, blend. Serve over fruit salad.

FRUIT DRESSING

1 avocado **juice ½ lemon**
1 papaya **1 tsp. kelp (optional)**
juice 2 oranges

Blend ingredients. Serve on fruit salad.

GOLDEN APPLE DRESSING

1 golden delicious apple **¼ cup lemon juice**
½ cup oil **1 tsp kelp**
¼ cup water

Pour water into blender. At slow speed, add diced apple. Blend in other ingredients.

HAWAIIAN PINEAPPLE

1 cup cubed pineapple **½ cup orange juice**
½ sour apple, diced

Blend ingredients at slow speed. Serve over citrus fruit or green salad. Makes 1 cup.

soups

Soups may be prepared with warm water if desired, and served in a pre-heated bowl.

BORSCHT

2 cups diced raw beets	1 lemon
1 green onion	½ cup almond, sesame
1 cup carrot or beet juice or water	or coconut butter

Liquefy ingredients in blender. Delicious as a soup or salad dressing.

CARROT BROTH

1 cup carrot juice	1 cup lentil sprouts
1 handful parsley leaves or buckwheat lettuce	1 handful watercress leaves or radish sprouts

Blend lentils to a pulp with a little water. Add carrot juice and other ingredients. Blend on low for a few seconds. Watercress and parsley have a strong characteristic odor and taste. Put into the blender a little at a time, and taste as you go along, to avoid making the soup too strong.

CARROT CREAM

¼ cup almond butter	½ tsp kelp
2 cups carrot juice	

Adding juice gradually, blend to a cream.

CARROT TROPICAL

1 med. carrot	½ tsp kelp
¼ cup coconut butter	¼ tsp ginger root
2 cups carrot juice	

Adding juice gradually, blend to a cream.

SPICY CORN

2 cobs sweet corn	1 avocado
3 sprigs watercress	1 tsp kelp
1½ cups warm water	

Cut corn from cob. Blend with water at low speed, to smooth consistency. Blend in avocado. Season with kelp. Serve with watercress sprinkled over top.

GAZPACHO I

2 large sliced cucumbers	3 large tomatoes, cubed
1 red pepper, cut fine	½ cup sliced celery
½ lemon	seasoning

Blend red pepper and celery with small amount of water. Season with 2 mint leaves or fresh ginger root (optional). Add lemon juice and follow with cucumber and tomato, using slow speed. Do not liquefy. Sea kelp may be added. For those who like it spicy, blend in some chives, onion, scallion, or one clove crushed garlic.

GAZPACHO II

2-3 ripe tomatoes	½ cup mixed vegetables
1 med. red pepper	and sprouts
1 tbs oil	1 tbs herb seasoning, kelp
water as needed	lemon or lime juice

Blend tomato , pepper, oil, water until smooth. Chop in vegetables and sprouts. Season.

MORNING MEADOWS

2 med. tomatoes	1 med. cucumber
1/6 avocado	2 oz. lime juice
¼ cup water	1 tbs kelp

Blend all ingredients and season to taste. Pour over bowl of avocado and tomato chunks and cucumber slices. Serve.

"Nothing frees the blood of disease-producing material so surely as pure air."
— Tilden, M.D.

POPEYE THE SAILOR

1 cup spinach   ½ avocado
1 cup sorrel   1 cup water

Blend greens with water. Add avocado. Season with mint, parsley, chives, onion or kelp. Serve as a dressing or as a soup.

VEGETABLE KINGDOM

1 cup vegetables   1 cup water
½ avocado   1 tsp. kelp

Choose one or two of the following vegetables: all tubers; weeds: sorrel, lambsquarters, sour grass, nettle; greens: parsley, comfrey, chard, spinach, celery. Blend and serve. In place of water, celery, tomato, cucumber or other vegetable juices may be used. For additional vitality add half a cup of your favorite sprouts.

TOMATO BASE

3 cups ripe tomatoes   1 small onion
1 med. carrot   ¼ cup almond or
½ pepper   sesame butter

Blend tomatoes, diced vegetables and butter to smooth consistency. Heat to temperature of human body, stirring constantly.

Sunflower — 1972

Vik — 1972

Vik — 1971

SPROUT SOUP

1 cup alfalfa sprouts   1 cup diced tomato
½ cup celery   1 tsp. oil

Blend celery and alfalfa with a little water. Add tomato and oil. Season to taste with your favorite herbs or dulse leaves.

spreads

Spreads may be served on lettuce leaves - rolled - or as side dishes to salads and sprout meals as well as dips and snacks. The spreads are concentrated foods and should be used in moderation. It is not food for babies or those with weak digestions. This observation is true for all concentrated foods - seeds, nuts, grains, legumes. Such foods become predigested through sprouting or fermentation and are easy on digestion. In the preparation be sure the seeds and nuts are fresh. If old they can be rancid and moldy. When fermenting, it is important to use pure water free of impurities. The yogurt and rejuvilac should have a very pleasant fragrance. If it smells or tastes bad, an error has been made in the preparation. All seed preparations which require an electric blender or grinder can be created with manual seed grain mill. Adjust it for fine grind. Mix water with seed flour. Then pour it into deep dish, cover it with cloth and place it in warm spot for fermentation.

RAW TOFU

Blend sprouted soy beans (or soybeans soaked for 24 hours and rinsed with just enough Rejuvilac to make a thick cream. Set in a warm place for 5-8 hours. Season to taste with kelp and herbs. Press the soy through a cheese cloth.

NUT BUTTER

1 cup nuts or seed, raw, unsalted
2 tbs. water

Grind to a paste in   grinder.   Mix in water with fork for a more creamy consistency. Superior butter may be produced just by running whole seed through the Health Fountain juicer. The butter may be seasoned with your favorite herbs or spices such as onion, chives, garlic or celery.

CRUNCHY BUTTER

1 cup nut butter   **¼ cup sesame seed**

Soak sesame seed for 5 hours. Using fork, mix drained seed into nut butter. This gives the butter extra taste, body and nutrition.

CASHEW CHEESE

Soak cashew nuts 12 hours. Blend one part water to one part cashews. Set in warm place 6 to 10 hours. Serve with green vegetable, indoor greens or sprout salad.

SUNFLOWER YOGURT

1 cup of freshly ground sunflower   **1 cup warm water**

   Pour sunflower into blender container using high speed, pour in slowly the rejuvilac. Blend to a creamy consistency. To hasten the ferementation, may add some of the previsouly made yogurt. Set in warm place. Cover, do not seal. Let it ferment to the desired sourness. Usually ready in 6 to 10 hours. May use the quart size electric yogurt maker. The ferment is ready in 5 hours. Let it cool down by removing it from the unit. This yogurt is one of the finest easily assimilable predigested protein. It taste like the traditional yogurt. Add kelp to taste. Serve with favorite sprouts. **Most folks would benefit to have the whey removed by pouring the yogurt into a cheese cloth bag or a fine strainer; let the liquid drip out. This eliminates most of the undesireable lactic acid.**

FESTIVITY RED FERMENT SAUCE

1-½ c. (cup) hulled sunflower seed   **3 c. water**
1 medium peeled/diced beet

Place seeds in blender (cheapest, best build is the Osterizer or obtain one with pyrrex glass top; avoid plastic). Blend until finely ground; shut off. With knife loosen the impactions of seed in blade and bottom of container. Add 1 cup water; blend on high until sauce thickens; slowly pour in another cup of water; let it thicken again (central whirlpool in sauce disappears). Continue adding liquid. Final product should be consistency of very heavy cream. To taste, add 2 cloves garlic, beets (in emergency may use the cooked commercial bottled beets, 2 to 4), juice of 2 lemons (remove the seeds), 3 oz. tamari or miso (source of bacteria for fermentation process). The tamari has salt and should be used in moderation or replaced with kelp and the water replaced with rejuvelac. May serve the sauce immediately, or to improve the taste as well as have it enriched with vitamin B complex and have the protein predigested, allow the sauce to sit for at least 8 hours in warm area (75 to 85 deg F) and have the bacteria act on the seed milk. The fermentation reduces the mucus forming of seed milk. The seed sauce may be kept in refrigerator for up to one week. Shake it before using it. This sauce is one of the most delicious one to add to sprout salads and introduce others to sprouts. I use this dressing at conventions.

PEANUT BUTTER

1 cup sprouted peanuts

   Run peanuts through grass juicer. Place in a bowl and mix in enough water to make a paste. Season to taste with kelp and/or diced onion, minced celery, green pepper or chives, or sprouted garlic.

special treats

ASPARAGUS BANQUET

10 spears tender asparagus

Place asparagus in a glass jar with radish roses serving as heads for the greens. Slice a few radishes into thin discs, and place in center of bouquet. Serve with sesonnaise or any of the protein sauces.

BEET TREET

3 med. beets	**¼ cup water**
½ cup safflower oil	**2 oz. lime juice**
2 tsp. kelp	**½ tsp. honey**

Shred beets, using No. 3 blade of griscer, or fine hand grater. Place 1 cup shredded beet, including unshredded portion, into blender with remaining ingredients. Blend to creamy consistency. Pour this sauce over the shredded beets and mix in. If in preparing sauce, you find it has a strong beet taste, add more lime juice or oil. Variations: add one small carrot to blender to produce pink sauce; replace the lime and honey with pineapple; replace water with tomato; mix Spanish onion, diced very fine, or chives with the shredded beets.

TURKISH TUNA

1 cup sesonnaise	**1 cup alfalfa sprouts**
½ cup diced celery	**¼ cup lentil sprouts**
¼ cup mung sprouts	**1 tbs. kelp**

Pour a little water into blender. Blend in celery at low speed. Add mung and lentils. Blend at low speed until they are just chopped. Pour all ingredients into bowl and mix thoroughly with fork. Season with kelp..

CELERY STICKS

4 stalks celery	**1 cup homemade sesame butter**

Cut stalks into 3" pieces. Stuff celery with sesame butter.

COLD KRAUT

1 med. head cabbage	1 med. bell pepper, grated
2 grated celery stalks	1 med. carrot, grated
2 limes	½ tsp. honey
1 oz. water	2 tsp. kelp
3 oz. safflower oil	

Shred carrot, celery, pepper and cabbage, using No. 3 blade of griscer. Place all ungrated sections of the vegetables into blender, using at least half a cup of cabbage. Add oil, lime, water and honey. Blend to creamy consistency. Add kelp. Pour this dressing over the shredded vegetables. Mix in with fork and serve. Very easy to digest because of fine shredding. Tastes like sauerkraut.

FLYING SAUCERS

3 med. sliced cucumbers	½ avocado
2 lemons	seasoning

Put a small amount of water into blender. At slow speed add 2 cucumbers, skin and all. Blend to fine consistency. Work in avocado as thickener. Add enough lemon juice to obtain desired tartness. Season with dash kelp. For variation, use mint, sorrel, dandelion, parsley or scallions. With knife or griscer, slice a crisp cucumber into thin discs. Place at an angle in cucumber sauce.

FLOATING CUCUMBERS

2 fresh crisp cucumbers	3 parts lemon
1 part light oil	1 part honey
1 part kelp	

If not organic, remove skins from cucumbers and slice very thin. Mix enough dressing to cover cucumber and shake thoroughly. Pour over cucumber and let marinate 20 minutes before serving.

CUCUMBER BOUQUET

2 crisp cucumbers	6 nasturtium leaves,
1 med. carrot	6 blossoms

Slice 1 cucumber lengthwise into 6 pieces. Slice the other cucumber into very thin discs. Spear discs with lengthwise pieces and arrange in a low glass jar. In the center of the arrangement, place carrot sticks and nasturtiums. Eat plain or dipped in dressing.

DULSE STEW

1 cup mung sprouts	½ cup dulse leaves
¼ cup sunflower seed meal	small clove garlic
	(optional)

Chop dulse leaves. Cover with hot water in pre-heated bowl. Mix with room temperature mung sprouts and seed meal.

GUACAMALI

1 avocado, diced	2 tomatoes, diced
2 med sweet red peppers,	1 tsp. kelp
diced fine	1 lemon

Using a fork, blend avocado to a creamy consistency, leaving a few lumps for texture. Mix with lime and seasoning to taste. Add remaining ingredients. This may be used as a complete meal, a dressing, party dip, or may be wrapped in a lettuce leaf to make a raw sandwich. Optional vegetables which may be added are: 1 stalk chopped celery; 1 med. diced cucumber, in season; 6 tbs diced Spanish onion. Some like it hot: freshly minced chili pepper or the oil from a clove of crushed garlic.

MINERAL SLAW

1 cup grated carrots	1 cup grated rutabaga
1 cup radish sprouts	2 cups grated cabbage
½ cup grated parsnips	

Mix ingredients. Serve with sesame dressing.

MOCK CHEESE AND SNAILS

1 med. long neck butternut squash
10 fiddler head fern greens

Slice squash in rings. Arrange in center of serving dish. On the borders, place greens, which look like snails. Serve with sesonnaise.

"And joy follows a pure thought, like a shadow faithfully tailing a man, we are what we think, having become what we thought."

— Siddharta Guatama, Buddha

MOCK SPAGHETTI

2 handfuls buckwheat lettuce   **1 cup alfalfa sprouts**
                                               (six day old)

Cut off buckwheat heads. The stems are tender and should be six inches long or more. Mix alfalfa and buckwheat stems around the borders of the serving dish, arrange buckwheat heads in centre. For dressing, use sesame or Firebird sauce.

MOCK TUNA SALAD

1 cup 6-day alfalfa sprouts   **½ cup mung sprouts**
½ cup celery, diced very fine   **½ cup diced onion**
1 cup shredded lettuce   **(optional)**

2 cups sesonnaise or sesame sauce to give it desired consistency. Serve on a bed of lettuce. Mix vegetables thoroughly. No one will know it's not tuna. For additional deception sprinkle with paprika on serving. Convert to mock salmon by adding grated carrots. Add dulce and kelp to give a fishy taste.

STUFFED PEPPER

small red sweet peppers   **guacamali**
lettuce

Wash peppers and remove stem ends, veins and seed. Sprinkle inside with lemon juice. Stuff with guacamali. Serve in a dish of lettuce garnished with watercress. May use large peppers cut in half.

RADISH ROSE

4 or more red radishes

Using a sharp paring knife, cut off tips of radishes. Remove green stem. Make petal-shaped cuts around radish from the cut tip to the center. Place radishes in ice water for a few minutes and the petals will open. When serving, place in shallow dish surrounded by watercress or parsley.

"Only he whose soul is touched by love lives."

— Duono

easy lunch

Grass, for quick high

THERMOS MEAL

For a lunch to take to work, fill a wide mouth thermos with your favorite salad or sprouts. Put dressing in a smaller container. You will have a complete meal without relying on bread.

STUFFY PEPPER

1 very large bell pepper
½ cup alfalfa sprouts
1 tsp. kelp

4 tbs. celery, diced fine
½ cup soy cheese

Cut off top of pepper and remove seed and veins. Make several incisions into top of papper, making it easy to tear off pieces to give additional flavor to stuffing. Mix other ingredients, season to taste, adding lime if needed, and fill the pepper. Close it with the top, and wrap in wax paper. Add a teaspoon and send it to school with a youngster.

easy lunch drinks

OPEN SESAME

¼ cup sesame meal
1 banana

1 cup warm water
dash kelp

Blend to a malt at high speed.

ALMONDCOW

¼ cup almonds
dash kelp (optional)

2 cups warm water

Soak almonds overnight and remove skins. Blend with warm water.

SEED MILK

½ cup seed
dash kelp (optional)

1 cup warm water

Soak pumpkin, sunflower or sesame seed overnight. Blend in the morning.

BANANA SHAKE

¼ cup sunflower seed
1 cup rejuvelac

1 ripe banana

Blend seed with small amount rejuvelac. Blend in banana. Thin to desired consistency.

"If you eat living food, the same will quicken you, but if you kill your food, the dead food will kill you also."

— Jesus, Essene Gospel of John

sweet treats

Each one a separate meal. Good for parties.

BIRTHDAY CAKE

2 lbs. pitted dates
2 lbs. dried figs
2 lbs. raisins

6 ripe bananas
3 avocados
grated ginger root

Soak figs overnight. Run dried fruit through Health Fountain juicer. Mix with 3 mashed bananas, ginger root. Mold to whatever shape desired. Refrigerate until ready to serve. Mash avocado and remaining bananas for icing.

BIRTHDAY SALAD

3 lbs. pitted dates
2 lbs. raisins
6 ripe bananas

4 avocados, diced
grated ginger root

Slice dates and bananas. Mix all ingredients and serve. Much easier than making a cake. Tastes just as good. May substitute grated fresh coconut for avocado.

DATE PIE

2 large grated apples
1 large ripe banana

1 cup pitted dates
1 cup grated fresh coconut

Run dates through wheatgrass juicer. Mix with equal part of coconut and dates. Mix mashed banana and apple for filling. Spread mixture over crust. Sprinkle with coconut.

CANDY

1 part banana   3 parts dried fruit

Run dried fruit through meat grinder or wheatgrass juicer. Mash banana and mix with fruit. Aroma and flavor can be improved by adding minced ginger and vanilla. Form into balls or cylinders. Roll in grated coconut. Freeze for a couple of hours to solidify.

"Seek the angel of sunlight. Put off your shoes and your clothing and suffer the angel of sunlight to embrace all your body. Then breathe long and deeply, that the angel of sunlight may be brought within you. And the angel of sunlight shall cast out of your body all evil-smelling and unclean things which defiled it without and within. And all unclean and evil-smelling things shall rise from you, even as the darkness of night fades before the brightness of the rising sun."

—The Essene Gospel of Peace,
Prof. Edmond Szekely

FRUIT COOKIES

1 cup raisins	**1 cup dried figs**
1 cup dried apple	**1 cup prunes**
1 whole coconut	**2 bananas**

Shred coconut and spread in pan. Grind dried fruits together. Mix with banana. Pour into pan. Sprinkle with grated coconut. Refrigerate for several hours, then cut into pieces of desired size. Will keep in refrigerator for weeks.

STUFFED AVOCADO

Cut avocado in half. Remove pit. Fill with raisins and sprinkle with lemon. Can be eaten with a spoon. A good way to introduce avocado to those not familiar with its taste.

STUFFED PRUNES

Remove pits from large prunes (or dates) and stuff with grated coconut.

PARTY SNACKS

1. Bowls of raw nuts, sunflower, pumpkin seed.
2. Bowls of fresh and dried fruit.
3. Serve 3-day peanut sprouts with kelp.
4. Season sprouted wheat and chick peas with kelp and oil.
5. Make dips from sesame or avocado sauces spiked with garlic, onion or horseradish and colored with blended beets, spinach, red pepper or carrots and served with chapati.
6. Spreads served with cucumber slices, celery sticks.
7. Tray of celery and carrot sticks, broccoli and cauliflowerets served with appropriate dip.

fired foods on the transitional diet

If you feel a need for cooked food, eat it following a large leafy green-sprout salad. Use no citrus or vinegar in dressing. Best to avoid protein foods – seeds, nuts -- when including cooked food to the meal. Eat the food cooled to body temperature.

IRON POT MEALS

The Dutch Oven necessary for these dishes may be purchased in many second hand stores or at Sears and Roebuck. It is made of cast iron with a heavy, tight-fitting lid, and available in a variety of sizes. It is cheaper to operate than a regular oven and emits almost no odor. It is ideal for furnishing warm food for the student away from home, the lone roomer, the business girl, or the couple living on a meager pension in small quarters. It will eliminate hours of household drudgery as it requires only to be brushed out once a week. To prepare the iron pot for the evening meal, line bottom with flat stones or a grating to prevent vegetables from burning. Scrub all vegetables carefully with a vegetable brush, as the skins should be eaten. Baking times will vary. The following schedule may be used as a guide:

ONE HOUR: large beets, carrots, sweet potato, plantain, rutabaga (small or cut in half), turnip, potato.

HALF HOUR: Yellow sweet squash, jerusalem artichokes, parsnips, corn on the cob, peas, beans, banana in jacket, apple (corn and banana jackets will turn black).

If sliced thin, the vegetables are ready in 8 minutes. Have no more than 2 different cooked vegetables at a meal. Live food should always be the main dish, with cooked food used as a dessert. Allow vegetables to cool before eating. This is first choice of fired foods.

CHOW MEAL

1 lb. sprouted soy beans
3 cups celery
2 cups fresh peas
1 cup bamboo shoots (optional)
2 tbs. kelp
4 tbs. oil

2 cups onion
2 med. carrots
1 cup mushrooms
1 tbs. ginger root
3 tbs. millet flour
¾ cup potassium broth

Slice onions, celery, carrots, bamboo shoots, mushrooms. Add sprouts and peas. Simmer for 10 minutes. Add flour. Stir. Remove from fire. Add oil. Season to taste. Serve with steamed millet or rice. Serves 6 - 10.

CHOW MEIN

1 cup mung sprouts
1 cup lentil sprouts
1 cup mushrooms
2 cups sliced onions

1 cup chopped celery
¼ cup soy oil
kelp
grated ginger root

Gently simmer mushrooms, onions, sprouts and celery in a small amount of water for 7 minutes. Remove from fire. Add oil and seasoning. Serve over millet or brown rice.

INSTANT CHOW MEIN

1 cup chopped onions
6 cups mung sprouts
1 tsp. grated ginger root

4 tbs. olive oil
kelp to taste

Simmer onions in water 5 minutes. Stir in 4 cups mung sprouts. Steam until they are hot (barely cooked). Remove from fire. Stir in remaining ingredients.

EVENING MILLET

1 cup millet
1 med. diced onion
2 large stalks celery, diced
2 large ripe tomatoes, diced
1 mint leaf

3 cups water
1 cup rejuvelac
4 tbs. oil
1 tbs. kelp

Wash millet and soak in 3 cups water for 8 hours. Place in baking dish and add other ingredients. Cover and bake at moderate heat for at least one hour.

MILLET MILK

1 cup millet   2 cups water
dash kelp

If possible, obtain unhulled millet and sprout for 3 days. Blend and strain. If unhulled millet is not available, soak seed 8 hours. Blend, strain. Heat in double boiler to break down starches. Millet is the queen of grains. It is the only one that is alkaline and low in protein. Both of these characteristics are beneficial to health.

Instead of cooking the millet, grind the seed in a nut mill. Blend it with water to a thick cream. Place it in dish on oven turned to the lowest heat level. Keep it overnight. Have it for breakfast or lunch.

MILLET DELIGHT

1 cup millet   5 cups water
½ cup apples, bananas, chopped   1 tsp. kelp

Wash millet. Soak overnight in 5 cups water. Pour water into pot and bring to boil. Add other ingredients and boil for 3 minutes. Turn heat down and simmer until it no longer tastes starchy.

MILLET BANANA

½ cup hulled millet   1 ripe banana
1½ cups hot water   dash kelp

Soak millet overnight. Blend ingredients together. If it tastes too starchy, cook in double boiler over slow flame for 5 minutes. A very tasty alkaline dish.

MOCK MEAT BALLS

1½ cups cooked millet   ½ cup grated beet or
3 tbs. onions, chopped fine   carrot
2 tbs. ground parsley   ½ cup millet flour
   (fenugreek)   dash savory (optional)

Mix ingredients thoroughly. Form into balls. Roll in millet flour (made in Moulinex grinder). Place balls in oiled baking pan. Bake at 350° for 20 minutes or until brown. Or form into patties and heat in lightly oiled skillet. Serve with sprouts.

COCONUT RICE

1 cup brown rice   **1 grated fresh coconut**

Wash and soak rice overnight in 3 cups water. Bring to boil. Turn down heat and steam until rice is soft: Add coconut. Heat for 5 more minutes. Serve hot or cold.

SCRAMBLED-A-CORN

1 cup corn cut from cob	**4 tbs. chopped green onion**
3 tbs. millet milk (or water)	**2 tbs. oil**
3 tsp. millet flour (optional)	**1 tbs. kelp**

Mix ingredients and simmer over low flame for 5 minutes. Add oil upon serving. Serve with mung sprouts.

COOKED SQUASH

1 small yellow squash   **1 small butternut squash**

Remove seed from butternut squash. Slice both squash. Cover with water. Cook till soft. Serve with sprouts.

SOY LOAF

1 cup soy sprouts	**4 stalks celery**
4 med. carrots	**1 small beet (optional)**
2 med. onions	**seasoning**

Blend sprouts with water to a thick puree. Grate carrots--use no. 3 griscer blade, or fine hand grater. Chop celery, diced beet and onions in blender at low speed. Mix all ingredients in bowl. Season with kelp and herbs if desired. Pour into oiled baking pan and bake in moderate oven–about 350°--for one hour or until slightly brown. (For more rapid preparation, drop onto lightly oiled skillet to form patties. Cook slightly). Serve plain or with a small amount of oil and/or alfalfa sprouts.

Leftovers may be served cold or heated. This recipe is also delicious uncooked and can be used as a salad dressing or as a sandwich spread. For the spread, add more grated carrots and alfalfa sprouts. Other tasty variations: mung, chick, lentil sprouts. This loaf is satisfying to those who are changing from a diet of meat.

MOTHER'S DELIGHT

4 onions sliced into rings

3 cubed tomatoes

1 cup pea or mung sprouts

1 tbs. kelp

4 peppers cut lengthwise

3 carrots cut thin

4 tbs. oil

Place all ingredients except tomatoes into a baking dish. Mix and cover with water. Bake at 350° for 20 minutes. Mix in tomatoes and bake until carrots and peppers are soft. Upon serving add oil. Serve plain or with brown rice or millet.

LIMA LOAF

1 cup lima beans

1 large stalk celery, chopped

1 bell pepper

1 med. onion, chopped fine

kelp to taste

Soak beans overnight. Rinse and soak 12 hours longer. Mix ingredients and cover with water. Bake at 300° for 2 hours or until beans are soft.

Marcia Cohn (P.O. Box 69590, Los Angeles, Calif. 90069) is sprouting wisdom in classroom.

"And he charged him to tell no man."

— Luke 5:14

fired soups

RED POTATOES

2 cups potatoes, cut fine	2 tbs. oil
1 cup grated beet	1 tbs. kelp

Cover ingredients with water and bring to boil. Simmer until potatoes are soft. Add kelp and oil. Cool slightly.

BALTIC CARROTS

2 cups diced potatoes	minced parsley
2 stalks diced celery	2 tbs. olive oil
½ cup whole barley	kelp to taste
1 onion	

Soak barley for 8 hours. Cover potatoes, barley, celery and onion with 1 quart of water. Simmer over low flame for 1 hour. Add oil and season to taste. Serve.

HI POTASSIUM BROTH

celery tops and leaves	carrot tops
sliced onions	potato peels

Simmer for 1 hour and strain. Serve (can also be prepared raw by using a juicer--preserves valuable enzymes). May be drunk or used as a base for other preparations, such as sauce and dressings.

CREAMED MILLET

½ cup hulled millet	2 tbs. oil
1 cup carrots, shredded fine	1 tsp. kelp
1½ cups water	

Soak millet overnight. Pour water off and put one cup into blender. At high speed, add millet a little at a time until creamy. Add remaining water. Pour into double boiler. Cook on low flame for about 15 minutes, stirring continuously or until starchy taste has disappeared. Add more water if needed, shredded carrots, oil, kelp to taste. Cool slightly. Serve.

MON WHEAT

1 cup tender peas   ½ cup chopped celery
1 cup buckwheat   1 tbs. kelp

Steam peas and celery for 10 minutes. Place one cup soak water in blender with wheat. Blend thoroughly and strain. Pour back into the peas and celery. Add a dash of parsley. Bring to a boil. Remove from fire. Add kelp. Cool slightly and serve.

TUES ONION

3 large onions, chopped   2 diced carrots
1 cup chopped celery   3 cups water

Bring water to a boil. Cook carrots about 10 minutes or until slightly soft. Add remainder of ingredients. Simmer until celery is slightly soft. Season with kelp.

WEDNES LIMA

1 cup large lima beans   1 cup onion, chopped
1 cup sweet pepper, chopped   ½ cup celery, chopped

Soak beans 8 hours and skin. Cover ingredients with water and bring to boil. Simmer until beans are soft. Season with kelp.

THURS MILLET

1 cup millet   2 tbs. oil
½ cup okra   4 cups water
½ onion, cut fine   1 tsp. kelp

Wash millet thoroughly and soak overnight. Add onion. Bring to boil. Simmer for 30 minutes or until there is no starchy taste left in the millet. Before serving, add thinly sliced okra, oil and kelp.

FRI BARLEY

1 cup barley sprouts   1 cup water
1 cup alfalfa sprouts   2 tsp. kelp

Blend barley and water. Strain out pulp. Simmer for 3 minutes. Blend alfalfa with barley milk. Add kelp and serve slightly cooled.

bread

If you feel desire for grains, sprout them. But if you feel a desire for bread, these recipes are probably the most healthful.

ESSENE BREAD

"Let the angels of God prepare your bread. Moisten your wheat, that the angels of water may enter it. Then set it in the air, that the angel of air may embrace it. And leave it from morning to evening beneath the sun, that the angel of sunshine may descend upon it. And the blessings of the three angels will soon make the germ of life to sprout in your wheat. Then crush your grain, and make thin wafers, as did your forefathers when they departed out of Egypt, the house of bondage. Put them back again beneath the sun from its appearing, and when it is risen to its highest in the heavens, turn them over on the other side that they may be embraced there also by the angel of sunshine, and leave them there until the sun sets. For the angels of water, or air and of sunshine fed and ripened the wheat in the field, and they, likewise, must prepare also your bread. And the same sun which, with the fire of life, made the wheat to grow and ripen, must cook your bread with the same fire. For the fire of the sun gives life to the wheat, to the bread, and to the body. But the fire of death kills the wheat, the bread, and the body. And the living angels of the living God serve only living men. For God is the God of the living, and not the God of the dead." (Essene Gospel of John, translated by E. Szekely)

If you don't like it made this way, you can always use the ground wheat sprouts for fired chapatis. Mix a little kelp into dough. Tastes very sweet—very rough texture.

CHAPATI

3 cups whole wheat flour OR	1½ cup water
2 wheat, 1 rice OR	kelp to taste
½ corn meal, ½ cracked wheat,	
¾ buckwheat OR	
2 wheat, 1 rolled or	
3 buckwheat, hulled	

Mix flour and kelp. Stir in enough water to make a stiff dough. Knead dough on a floured table until smooth and satiny. Cover with a moist cloth and let set for 1 hour. Break off dough into 1 inch balls and roll out to form patties 7" in diameter. Bake on both sides on lightly oiled pan over low heat. May add wheat sprouts to any of the combinations.

CORN CHAPATI

2 cups corn meal	kelp to taste
1½ cups water	

Mix all ingredients. Let set 30 minutes. Drop onto lightly oiled skillet.

AVOCADO BUTTER SANDWICH

1 avocado	1 tbs. chopped onion
½ cup alfalfa sprouts	1 tsp. kelp

Spread avocado on a chapati. Slice a few rings of avocado and place on chapati. Add alfalfa, kelp, onions. Serve as open face sandwich or use two chapati.

BUTTERED BANANA

1 ripe banana	3 tbs. almond butter

Peal and slice banana lengthwise into 3 pieces. Spread almond butter on a chapati and top with as much banana as will fit.

"Suffer little children to come unto me, for of such is the Kingdom of God."
— Luke 18:16

transitional diet

Prepare each meal more simply than the previous one but always make it tasty and colorful.

Although I do not recommend eating between meals, if you feel hungry, take herb tea, juice or fruit. Take grass juice once a day.

Viktoras 1977

MENUS FOR ONE DAY

BREAKFAST
Choice of One

Fruit salad
Fruit drink
Fruit juice
Grass juice

Dried fruit, raw
Dried fruit, steamed
Seed milk
Vegetable juice mixture

LUNCH

Sprout and vegetable salad or

Fruit salad

SUPPER

Sprout and leafy green salad with dressing.

Iron pot meal.

4-12 ounces vegetable juice

therapeutic diet

This diet should be followed for at least 2 weeks. Improvement in health will become evident in 5 days. For one week stay on a live food diet. Then repeat the therapeutic diet for two weeks. After a month you may introduce a water fast for one day each week.

Avoid avocado, oil, seed, seasonings. Eat small quantities. Blend or juice the salad if you have difficulty chewing.

If you have a severe problem, you should do a wheatgrass juice fast. Use the therapeutic diet, replacing the evening meal with watermelon or other juice fruit. If feel hungry in between meals, drink live vegetable grass or weed juice.   Follow rules For Best Digestion (Pgs 5, 9).

MORNING

1 cup tea, water, limeade or rejuvilac
shower
5–20 minutes deep breathing
meditation and prayer
yoga or other exercise
wheatgrass juice plain or mixed
enema and grass juice implant

LUNCH

1 glass lemonade
30 minutes later: wheatgrass juice
1 hr. later: watermelon or another non-acid juicy fruit

MID-AFTERNOON

Exposure to sun
Deep breathing
Grass juice

SUPPER

Sprout and leafy green salad
OR
Fruit salad
OR
Vegetable juice

Live Food Diet

A diet of sprouts, indoor greens, weeds and dehydrated sea vegetables can be tasty and can supply you with all the needed nutrients for optimal health. Sprouted seed creams and cheeses, as well as fruit, can be added in for extra protein and variety.

sample menu for one day

breakfast	lunch	supper
water or herbal tea	green juice	
20 minutes later	20 minutes later	fruit or sprout salad
grass or green juice	sprout and leafy green salad	or green strength soup
or fresh fruit or	seed cream	
seed cream vegetable blend		
or seed cream fruit smoothy		

BODY BUILDING PROGRAM

This program has been successful for wieght and strength increase with children as well as adults in their 40's, plus. Follow a theraputic diet for at least 3 weeks. Exercise daily for a minimum of one hour, five times a week and get adequate rest.

Breakfast	lunch	Supper
herbal tea	4–8 cups green juice	8 oz. green juice from
30 minutes later	30 minutes later	mixture of indoor
1 cup sprouted seed cream	1 cup of purple cream	plants and other vegetables
1 ripe banana	2 cup of sprouts and other vegetables	mix into it 8 oz. seed cream.
or 1 — 2 cups of	or Greeen Strength Soup	Add spices, kelp
Green Strength Soup	see page 56	and nutritional yeast(optnl)

Other variations: At least 5 times a week use 2–day sprouted cereal, such as oat, barley, rye or wheat. Blend to cream 1 cup water and 1 cup cereal. May strain out the milk or use all. Blend in 1 super ripe banana (optional). Chew each mouthful very well.

Weight gain will take place only if your digestion works well and you have cleaned up your body. Do not attempt to overeat or eat too often. No snacks. Eat only when hungry. Take one day off each week to fast on green juice. On such a program the author gained 20 pounds in 2 months.

MOTHER CHILD DIET

Pregnant mothers should not make any radical changes in diet, instead follow the transition suggestions on page 7. Happy, loving low stress attitude is central. Raising a child is a full time love activity. Much can be gained by considering chastity during pregnancy and weaning. After 3–24 months of breast feeding, diluted fruit juice, as well as green juice mixed with apple, pear or carrot may be introduced. Best food for baby is breast milk from a mother on a good diet. When introducing solid food, blend, juice or pre–chew. Spoon feed the child. Stay away from starchy or complex protein foods. Instead feed milks made from predigested (fermentation or sprouting) sprouted wheat, seed cheese, sunflower sprouts. See Survival Into 21st Century for additional details.

— appendix —

A FEW FAVORITE FOODS

Although the live food way needs no nutrition tables, we include a few comments upon properties of certain especially recommended foods, and cautions for use of other popular ones.

Fruit is the most perfect food. A mono-meal of apples, oranges, plums or pears can be a satisfying treat. Fruit acids do not make the body acid. Rather, they increase the alkalinity of the body. Healthy urine, saliva, blood, extracellular fluid and cytoplasm are all slightly alkaline. Protein, starch and fat foods are acid-forming, while fruits, as well as vegetables, render the urine alkaline.

According to Dr. Shelton, "There is a constant addition of acid to the extracellular fluid. As a consequence, the urine of man is acidic, as compared with extracellular fluid. The compensatory control exerted by the kidney prevents sodium loss, and normal extracellular fluid is remarkably constant in composition and volume as well as pH. Subsistence on a diet which consists largely of fruit and vegetables, results in the opposite situation, i.e., addition to the extracellular fluid of an excess of alkali, which is eliminated in the urine. The kidney regulates the alkaline-acid balance of the body. If there is an excess of acid, then the urine will have an acid reaction. In the case of a fruit diet, the urine is alkaline, hence the body is not being acidified."

Apples are an excellent food: alkalinizing, cleansing, easy to digest; stored sun vibrations available in the north all winter.

Avocado, although rich in minerals and vitamins, containing about two percent protein, is about 13.4 percent fat, therefore difficult to digest. One should not eat more than half an avocado a day. Those who are on a cleansing diet or those with liver disorders should avoid avocado. Do not eat it combined with sesame and sunflower seed or other protein foods. It combines best with leafy greens.

Grapes are high in sugar, potassium and iron and predominate in alkaline elements. For an effective cleansing mono-diet, generally take one pound of grapes every three to four hours for a week.

Lemon (lime) is one of the best foods for cleansing the bloodstream. It loosens and precipitates out, the extraneous alkaline mucus to be eliminated from the body. Observe this in your mouth: hold a mouthful of lemon water for one minute. Then spit it out and you will see the white stringy mucus which has been precipitated out. Drinking lemonade regularly will result in a less viscous bloodstream of higher oxygen content, which will reflect in clearer thinking. The acid pH of fruit is excellent during the cleansing period. Lemon drink is the best remedy for a cold. (The cleansing illness). Because of pH, lemon juice will also dissolve out excessive calcium and lime deposits of arthritis.

Watermelon (Melon, cubes) are noted for their alkaline pH and high predominance of alkaline minerals, generally at least three times more alkaline than acid. They are a very rich source of potassium. They are valuable in kidney disorders because they induce diuretic action. They combine badly with ALL other foods, and should be eaten alone or on an empty stomach.

Never throw away the rind. The green skin of watermelon is high in chlorophyl and alkaline minerals. Hand juice the rind, then drink it. You can blend it and soak your feet in it, put it in your bath. It feels refreshing, as it alkalinizes your cells via osmotic pressure.

Grains: Millet is the queen of grains, the only one which is alkaline-forming in the body, therefore it does not leach calcium from the tissues. During the transition to raw food, millet is an economical, tasty grain. Pythagorus himself, who advocated a low protein diet for spiritual, intellectual and physical development, used millet as a basic food. Cook on radiator or low flame overnight.

Millet, when cooked, releases a bland, soothing, mucilaginous substance which acts as an intestinal lubricant, aiding elimination. It is one of the easiest grains to digest. Drs. Osborne and Mendel found that millet contains all essential vitamins and minerals. They found that millet is unique among grains in that it contains all essential amino acids and therefore furnishes a complete protein. It is high in lecithin, an essential component of nerve tissue. Millet is flavorful when eaten by itself without salt or fat.

Wheat is a staple food all over the world. However, in cooked form it is a destroyer of health; many people are allergic to it, it can cause mucus congestion and constipation. Wheat contains an abundance of acid minerals, which reduces alkaline reserves. It can leach calcium from bony tissues.

In sprouted form, wheat becomes an acceptable food. Much of the starch is converted to simple sugars. The vitamin E content triples. Vitamin C is increased by a factor of six. In the vitamin B-complex, the individual vitamins increase ranges from 20 to 1200 percent.

The best use of wheat is to grow it as grass. The solid content of the juice is up to 70 percent chlorophyl. The enzyme contect is maximum at this stage. Like most whole foods, it is rich in Laetrile (the anti-cancer vitamin B-17), which can selectively destroy cancer cells, but has very little effect on normal cells. According to Dr. Krebs, the Laetrile content in sprouts and greens increases up to 100 times more than that of the seed from which they originate.

Legumes (including peanuts) of every kind are acid-forming unless sprouted, because of a high concentration of protein and starch and low moisture content. Sprout them.

Mung Sprouts If man were to eat food best suited to his physiology he would eat fruit and succulent green. After three days of growth, mung sprouts become like a fruit in many ways.

According to **Composition of Foods, U.S.D.A.**, we can make the following observations about mung sprouts: The moisture of the seed increases from 10.7 percent to 88.8 percent in the sprout, comparable to any fruit. Protein is converted to amino acids, and its concentration is reduced to that of a dried fig. The germination process converts starch to simple sugars. The carbohydrate content of mung bean sprouts is the same as in casaba melon. The caloric value is slightly less than that of papaya and a little more than that of honeydew melon. One cup, or one fourth pound, contains forty calories. Sprouted mung has the vitamin A value of a lemon, thiamin of an avocado, riboflavin of dried apple, niacin of a banana and ascorbic acid of a pineapple.

Alfalfa Sprouts, after seven days of growth, are an excellent source of chlorophyll. Like all sprouts, they are a rich source of vitamins A, B-Complex and C. They can also provide you with vitamins D, E, G, K and U. The roots of alfalfa extend up to 100 feet into the earth, gathering a wide range of minerals. Dr. Sherman Davis of the University of Indiana has pointed out that alfalfa is especially rich in iron, calcium and phosphorus. Dr. Edward Mellenby of England reports that "alfalfa is essential to rebuild decayed teeth." (**Nature's Healing Grasses,** H. E. Kirchner, M.D.) Alfalfa sprouts contain all the essential amino acids.

Soybean is a highly alkaline legume, almost a complete food, hence noted for its versatility. It contains a complete well-balanced protein of high biological efficiency.

However, it is a highly concentrated food and should be eaten in moderation. Avoid pre-cooked preparations, and use only sprouted soybeans for increased vitamin content, increased digestibility and best health.

Nuts eaten in too great an abundance or inadequately chewed, can be very hard to digest. Eat them in careful combination, preferably with leafy greens; chew or blend them to a milk for best digestion.

Cashew, especially, is not readily digestible--it is similar to a legume. However, when made into a cheese, it becomes easy to digest.

Sesame Seed is a staple food in the Mediterranean area. It is a concentrated complete protein, easy to use raw as a butter, sauce, soup, cheese or milk. In the unhulled form, it contains ten times more calcium than cow's milk, one and a half times more iron than beef liver, three times more phosphorus than eggs, more protein than chicken, beef liver or beefsteak, and more niacin than whole wheat bread. (**Composition of Foods, Handbook No. 8, U.S.D.A.**)

Sunflower Seed is a rich source of vitamins D, B-6, B-12 and all the essential amino acids. The protein is highly concentrated--use no more than two ounces per day.

Growing it in soil for seven days increases the enzyme content manyfold, converts the fat to carbohydrates and transforms the complex protein into easily digested amino acids.

Seeds, Enzymes, and Oxalic Acid: Water activates the enzymes in seeds making the produce easier to digest. Sesame requires only soaking, sprouting makes it bitter. Sesame hull has high oxalic acid level - eliminate it by blending the seeds to a cream, followed by straining off the hulls with a sprouting bag or strainer. Sunflower and pumpkin can be sprouted up to 8 hours. Almond and other non-oily nuts should be sprouted for at least 24 hours.

Alkaline Foods such as sprouts, seed creams [p41], indoor greens, sweet non−acid fruit, most vegetables should make up 80% of your diet. Acid fruits, grains, nuts, seed cheeses [p56], rejvilac, sauerkraut, bakery products should not exceed 20% of your daily diet intake.*Cooked Foods*:First soak and sprout for 12 hours all grains, 2−4 days all legumes. Then in cooking use low temperature, very little water withsteaming or baking and allow the food to soften and/or sweeten without destroying the fiber. Use no oils. Experiment with a dehydrator in creating breads and other heavier dishes.

— *food combining for easier digestion* —

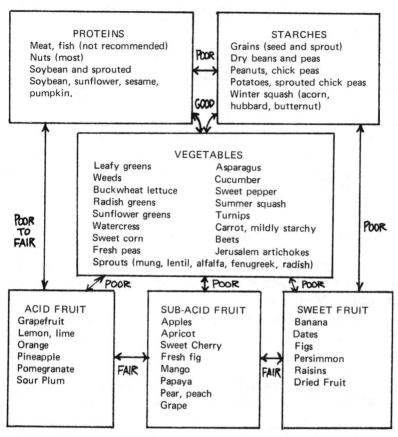

PROTEINS
Meat, fish (not recommended)
Nuts (most)
Soybean and sprouted
Soybean, sunflower, sesame,
pumpkin.

POOR

GOOD

STARCHES
Grains (seed and sprout)
Dry beans and peas
Peanuts, chick peas
Potatoes, sprouted chick peas
Winter squash (acorn,
hubbard, butternut)

VEGETABLES

Leafy greens
Weeds
Buckwheat lettuce
Radish greens
Sunflower greens
Watercress
Sweet corn
Fresh peas
Sprouts (mung, lentil, alfalfa, fenugreek, radish)

Asparagus
Cucumber
Sweet pepper
Summer squash
Turnips
Carrot, mildly starchy
Beets
Jerusalem artichokes

POOR
TO
FAIR

POOR

POOR

POOR

POOR

ACID FRUIT
Grapefruit
Lemon, lime
Orange
Pineapple
Pomegranate
Sour Plum

FAIR

SUB-ACID FRUIT
Apples
Apricot
Sweet Cherry
Fresh fig
Mango
Papaya
Pear, peach
Grape

FAIR

SWEET FRUIT
Banana
Dates
Figs
Persimmon
Raisins
Dried Fruit

GOOD COMBINATIONS
Protein and leafy greens
Starch and vegetables
Oil and leafy greens
Oil and acid fruit
Oil and subacid fruit

POOR COMBINATIONS
Protein and acid fruit
Leafy greens and acid fruit
Leafy greens and subacid fruit

BAD COMBINATIONS
Protein and starch
Oil and protein
Starch and fruit

83

GUIDELINES FOR BEST DIGESTION

ONE food at a meal FOR BEST DIGESTION. Or combine according to chart.

OIL slows digestion. Combine best with non-sweet fruit and vegetables; poorly with starch and protein. Best source of oil is whole seed.

AVOCADO combines best with fruit, tomato, green vegetables or sprout.

WHEATGRASS is best chewed (spit out the pulp) or drunk as juice on an empty stomach. May be mixed with vegetable juices, or juices from indoor salad greens, alfalfa and fenugreek sprouts.

GREEN LEAFY VEGETABLES aid fat and protein digestion.

HONEY AND MOLASSES (best to avoid) should be taken alone on an empty stomach. Otherwise, may cause gas, indigestion or headache.

ALL RIPE ORGANIC FRUIT produce an alkalizing effect on bloodstream. Acid forming foods are the nuts, (meat, fish, egg, cheese), seeds, grains, with only few exceptions.

DAIRY PRODUCTS (best to avoid) should be taken alone. Use raw. Yogurt is the best choice - be sure it is not pasteurized after fermentation.

TOMATO combines best with vegetables, avocado, oil; fair to poor with acid fruit. Should be used only in season, otherwise it is acid forming.

JUICE of tomatoe, citrus, apple and carrot may be added to the nonstarchy vegetable juices to improve the taste. Since juice is absorbed in 20 minutes it will not cause digestive complications due to fermentation resulting from such mixture in a salad. It is very important to chew all foods including juices. A liquid drink is a meal and should be consumed only on an empty stomach. A solid meal can be followed 30 minutes later or when feeling hungry. Most benefit from juice is obtained when drunk in small quantity (4 to 8 oz) every hour. Juice should be pulp free. Strain it if there is any sediment.

"After the angel of air, seek the angel of water. Put off your shoes and your clothing and suffer the angel of water to embrace all your body. Cast yourselves wholly into his enfolding arms, and as often as you move the air with your breath, move with your body the water also. I tell you truly, the angel of water shall cast out of your body all uncleannesses which defiled it without and within. And all unclean and evil-smelling things shall flow out of you, even as the uncleannesses of garments washed in water flow away and are lost in the stream of the river. I tell you truly, holy is the angel of water who cleanses all that is unclean and makes all evil-smelling things of a sweet odour. No man may come before the face of God, whom the angel of water lets not pass."

—The Essene Gospel of Peace,
Prof. Edmond Szekely

poor man's healthful organic diet on 2¢ per meal.*

Lbs./year	Cost/year	Food item: dry	Garden	Food Item live	Convsn ratio	Cost/unit live	Hrs. soak	Days grow	Dry seed in garden	Food usage	Live food per day
40	9.00	buckwheat	17"x25" tray	buckwheat lettuce	1:4	4c/Lb.	3	7	¾ lb/tray	salad, juice sauce, soup	½ Lb.
30	8.00	sunflower greens	" "	sunflower	1:5	5c/Lb.	3	7	½ lb/tray	" "	½ Lb.
100	10.00	wheat	" "	wheatgrass juice	1:4	10c/Qt.	12	7	¾ lb/tray	juice, rejuvelac	¼ lb. or 4 oz. juice
16	6.90	mung	qt. jar mason	sprouts	1:6	7c/Lb.	20	2-4	¼ cup/jar	juice, salad casserole or sauce	1/3 lb.
3	2.20	alfalfa	"	sprouts	1:8	9c/Lb.	3	3-8	2 tbs./jar	juice, salad tea	1/3 lb.
4	2.00	kelp		seasoning						seasoning	1 tsp.
22	8.80	sesame	gallon cans	sprouts	1:2	18c/Lb.	12	1		cheese, milk sauce, soup	1 oz.
12 rts.	3.00	comfrey (kale) Root		green vegetable						tea, sauce soup	3/16 lb.
365 qts.	11.00	home distilled water									1 qt.

TOTAL: $61.00 for one year

SOURCES: For staples: Pejoneer, Erewhon and Organic Gardens, 1972 Prices

UTENSILS: Mannual grass juicer - grind sesame & sprouts, juice greens, extract oil

DISTILLER: Gives you pure water. Use only stainless steel or glass

RECYCLE: Don't waste your garbage, vegetable dung, or urine. Return it and it will make beautiful food and flowers

Purchase seeds and tools from a coop, or obtain a wholesale license from the Department of Commerce for one dollar. It will mean at least a 35% saving.

On this COMPLETE MEAL SALAD DIET you would get daily at least two pounds of food, which includes 4 ounces of grass juice. The cost is $61.00 (18c per day) per year. MOre money can be saved. A distiller can be operated on free fire wood (save $11). For most health seekers, this type of diet, within one year would become too elaborate and too filling. Generally, one pound daily of live food would be adequate for high vitality (save $26.00). For best health, a weekly fast of 36 hours is a must (save $4.45). During summer, autumn and spring, one can obtain at least one half of food free from nature, gardening and abandoned orchards (save $8.80). This reduces ONE YEAR'S FOOD BILL TO $13.50 or 2c per meal.

*INFLATION has increased prices by about 50% since first printing in 1972. In 1978, the cost has increased to about 4¢ per average meal.

*In 1980, the inflation has raised the cost to about 8 cents per average weekly meal.

zone therapy

The Ancient Masters recognized the body as a symphony of divine vibrations. The internal organs orchestrate the energy from sun, air, water, food and friends to give joy and life to the soul on earth. The blood carries the life force into each of the cells. The nerves, capillaries, lymph, arteries, skin are the channels through which the life force harmoniously flows.

If the Life Force is blocked, or does not flow with body's life rhythm, one becomes old and sick, regardless of age. This will happen, when any one of the body's members are hurt because of breaking of Nature's Health Laws. It will show up as constipation, congestion, retention of poisons, toxemia.

Zone Therapy, foot massage, acupuncture, contact healing, chiropractic, osteopathy are different methods for increasing energy, establishing energy balance, breaking up sedimented acid crystals and improving circulation.

During dietary transition or binge or breaking of health laws you will find zone therapy will minimize discomforts, and in many cases eliminate the symptoms or causes of disease.

There are zones of release in your feet, hands, head, scalp, back of the neck, colon and most areas of the body. The chart will help you. Work on your feet at least for 5 minutes, three or more times a week. If the areas are sensitive or painful, it indicates they are not normal, and work on them should be continued daily. Special emphasis should be placed on the digestive areas. Extra firm pressure can be applied by putting full weight of the foot onto a golf ball (appropriately placed) or stone. A heavy duty twist cap coke bottle, filled with very warm water, can be stepped onto or rolled onto, with the full weight of your foot.

Before you use this pressure therapy, you should soak the feet in hot water (sea salt added) for ten minutes.

Uncooked living food and juice fast should be utilized with this therapy for permanent results. The cause of the trouble must be removed before one can enjoy the fruits of youthful health.

ADDITIONAL AIDS: To increase the elimination of toxins, stay on fluid diet for at least three hours before zone therapy, and at least 5 hours after. You should work on the feet for at least twenty minutes. Use color to change the energy in your Astral Body. The color of food, clothing, lights and juices changes your emotions, vitality and health. Red increases vigor and is an aid to elimination. Blue will calm, relax, reduce pain. Green will balance your body life force. Yellow increases your circulation and the function of your mind. The best source of color is the Sun. Spend daily at least 30 minutes in the sun.

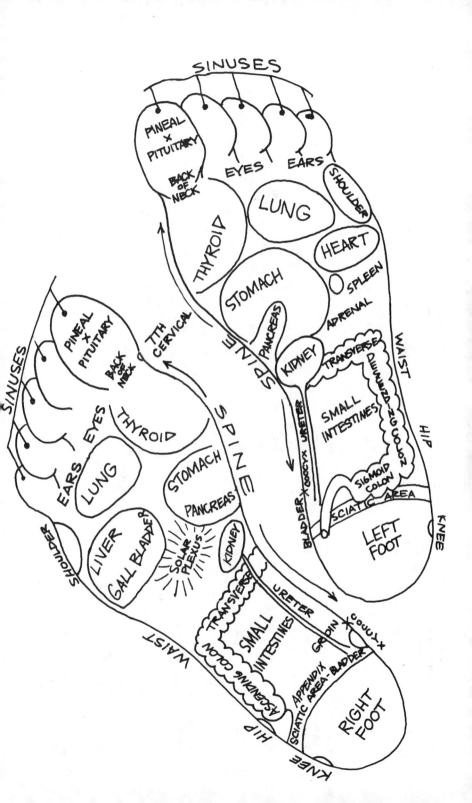

LIFE IN THE 21st CENTURY
Compiled by Viktoras Kulvinskas
Illustrated by Jean White

Contributions span a five year period and represent the most up-to-date experimental living centered around living food and the spiritual path as a precursor for the life of communion with God and our blissful inheritance. You will read about 200 stories from over a hundred authors from all over the world. Many articles by Viktoras.

The following are just a few of the headlines of the text: New Age Communities – Letters from Hawaii, California, Kentucky, Oregon, Belize, Guatemala, Bolivia, Costa Rica, Ecuador, Venezuela, Australia, Puerto Rico, West Indies, New Zealand, Fiji, and Bombay.

Special articles on a diversity of subjects from the raw foodist point of view: Six detailed stories of childbirth and raising of raw foodist children. experimentation...Raw foodist experience in Toronto, Wisconsin, etc....Testimonials of healing on the full spectrum of ailments...Sister Susan Kuruvilla, breatharian for 10 years, Biography and photoes...Physiology of Breathing. Tantric Master, 20 years on wheat sprouts and wheatgrass – one pound a day – and no other food. Looks like he's in his late 20's and is actually over 50 years of age...
Birth control from plant kingdom...

21st Century Chef **Brother Rom Pickarski** the best known vegetarian chef, who is competing in the 1980 Chef Olympics, was on the cover of Vegetarian Times...

Into the eighties, Mark Brounstein, Author of "Radical Vegetarian"...
Teeth show that natural diet of man was fruit – NY Times, 1979...
Research on Pyramids and Kirlian Photography and the affects on wheatgrass...
Bio Music and Psychic Kiss.

Effect of Light and Color on humans...
Pineal body and research into spirituality...
Man made dangers and how to survive. Radiation, alluminum, oil, soil, air...
Warning from suicide victim...

Life lights – wheatgrass evangelist and school bus gypsies of California...
Brain – Biological resistance against institutional nuts...
Human survival insurance policy...
Paradise lost, looking for an ideal place...
Planting fruit and nut trees on public land...
Telling millions about vegetarianism on pennies...
How to be a vegie activist in your college...
Run across the USA from Florida to California by two sproutarians...
Ancient secrets for eternal youth...

Hazards of nuclear power and how to protect oneself...
Danger of eating oil, even raw...
Story on Viktoras...
Religion, diet and health...
Time for us to become masters...
Emotions can heal...
Facts on Comfrey. Medicinal use of onion...
Evidence of Intestinal Toxemia, over 200 medical journals cited...
Curative crises, elimination and enemas...
Shatkriyas of Traditional Hatha Yoga – by 50 year old nuclear physicist who looks under 30, many photoes and details on how to clean the whole of the intestinal tract. Key to longevity...
Death in exchange of fine, African Myth...
Arthritis, cause and cure...
Raw Vegetarianism and Cancer cure...
Raw foodist humor, poetry, short stories...
How to stay forever high, chemistry of bliss...
Fasting – dry, wet, juice, water long, short...

400 pages, 6 by 9 in., $14.95

Meal For Famine or Feast

RAW FOOD MOTHERS

Please share with us your stories and experiences on a pregnancy, birthing, diet, chastity. We will be including it in our publication on New Age children, birth control through diet, control of menstruation. Your contribution would be a great help and an inspiration to all mothers who are seeking best for their offsprings.

DIETARY TRANSITION WARNING

After many years observing individuals making diet changes on their own or under the guidance of a nutritionist, I feel some warnings have to be made to prevent undesirable side effects and discouragment.

Those persons who have followed traditional highly processed diet of high protein intake should observe some caution, especially if they are over 30. Use the diagnosis techniques to determine the state of your health as well as complete blood analysis - if that should be your inclination. Such toxic individuals would benefit from pursuing the gradual transition as suggested in the text, as well as in Love Your Body. Otherwise, extreme skin blemishes or sores, extensive hair loss, fatigue, as well as other symptoms may develop. All due to the overloading of the eliminative organs. These symptoms eventually clear up.

If rapid transition is desirable then the individual should have as needed unlimited rest, enemas, implants, salt baths, juices and fasting, preferably in a pollution free environment. For assured guidance, such a program should be under the supervision of an experienced natural food healer.

LEUCOCYTOSIS OF DIGESTION CAUSED BY COOKING

A study by Paul Kauchakoff (Suisse) M.D. of the Institute of Clinical Chemistry, Lausanne, Switzerland, revealed:

"After over 300 experiments on ten individuals of different age and sex, we have come to the following conclusion:
1. The augmentation of the number of white corpucles and the alteration of the correlation of the precentage between them which takes place after every consumption of food, and which was considered until now as a physiological phenomena, is, in reality, a pathological one. It is called forth by the introduction into the system of foodstuff altered by means of high temperatures, and by complicated treatments of ordinary products produced by nature. 2. After the consumption of fresh raw foodstuff, produced by nature, our blood formula does not change in any lapse of time, nor in consequence of any combination."

The critical temperature is not the same for all raw foodstuff. It varies within a range of ten degrees. The lowest critical temperature for water is 191; milk 191; cereal, tomatoes, cabbage, banana 192; potatoe 200; carrot, strawberry, fig 206 (all in Fahrenheit degrees). (from the Proceedings: First International Congress of Macrobiology, Paris 1930. Translated by Lee Foundation for Nutritional Research)

SPROUT A COMPLETE PROTEIN

There are two ways to establish whether a food item supplies a complete protein. First through biological studies using animals (or by observing cultural diet patterns of humans) who eat a controlled diet. If adequate protein is present, then the researchers expect a normal growth rate, absence of clasical protein deficiency diseases, longevity pattern of that species and healthy reproduction for at least several generations. Second, through chemical analysis.

By the first method, Dr. Francis Pottenger Jr. had found *"sprouted grain to be a complete protein in an animal test, completely servicing the reproduction program through generations (p. 40) . . . he had found sprouted legumes and grains to contribute enough first quality protein to be classed as complete (p. 295)."* Likewise, Dr. C.F. Schnabel showed grass is adequate in providing all needed nutrients, including protein, in animal experiments.

To establish by the second method one has to take the indirect approach because of lack of nutritional data on sprouts.

From the study of germination process, Drs. Mayer and Poljakoff-Mayber (Germination of Seed, Pergamon Press, 1963) of the Botony Dept. Hebrew University, Jerusalem, observed: *"Nitrogen (protein) appears to be very carefully conserved. In place of the protein broken down there appears free amino acids and amides."* That is, in germination, the amino acids are freed (not destroyed) from their protein structure. Hence, if a seed contains a complete protein then the sprout (of lower density due to the dilluting effect of water) can be anticipated to contain all the amino acids that were in the original seed protein.

From the following table (Amino Acid Content of Food, Orr and Watt, U.S.D.A., Wash., D.C.) we see that the listed seeds contain a complete protein. Hence the sprouts of the seeds are also complete proteins.

The table values are for raw produce. Pasteurized dairy produce, eggs and meat do not have the amino acids listed in the table when they are served in the cooked form. Without any considerations, if one is to search for a food item that would supply a complete protein, one would choose raw sprouted seeds.

	chick peas	lentil	muny	soy	wheat	buck wheat	sun flower
tryptophan	0.170	0.216	0.180	0.526	0.173	.17	0.343
threonine	0.739	0.896	0.765	1.504	0.403	.46	0.911
isoleusine	1.195	1.316	1.351	2.054	0.607	.44	1.276
leucine	1.538	1.760	2.202	2.946	0.939	.68	1.736
lysine	1.434	1.528	1.667	2.414	0.384	.69	0.868
methionine	0.276	0.180	0.265	0.513	0.214	.21	0.443
phenylalanine	1.012	1.104	1.167	1.889	0.691	.44	1.220
valine	1.025	1.360	1.440	2.005	0.648	.61	1.354
argine	1.551	1.908	1.370	2.763	0.670	.93	2.370
histidine	0.559	0.548	0.543	0.911	0.286	.26	0.586
total protein	28%	25%	24.4%	35%	14%	12%	23%

	soy sprout	buck sprout	sunf sprout	meat	human milk		date	egg	sesame
tryptophan		.03	.06	0.220	.103	.058	.06	.211	.33
threonine	0.017	.09	.15	0.830	.284	.257	.06	.637	.71
isoleusine	0.159	.09	.21	0.984	.344	.240	.07	.850	.95
leucine	0.225	.15	.30	1.540	.567	.475	.08	1.126	1.7
lysine	0.265	.16	.12	1.642	.413	.353	.07	.819	.58
methionine	0.211	.04	.07	0.466	.128	.051	.03	.401	.64
phenylalanine	0.045	.09	.20	0.773	.272	.142	.06	.739	1.5
valine	0.186	.12	.21	1.044	.391	.283	.09	.950	.89
argine	.225	.19	.30	1.212	.253	.172	.05	.840	1.9
histidine	.133	.05	.09	0.653	.138	.061	.05	.307	44
total protein	6%	2%	4%	19%	1.4%	.8%	2.2%	13%	19%

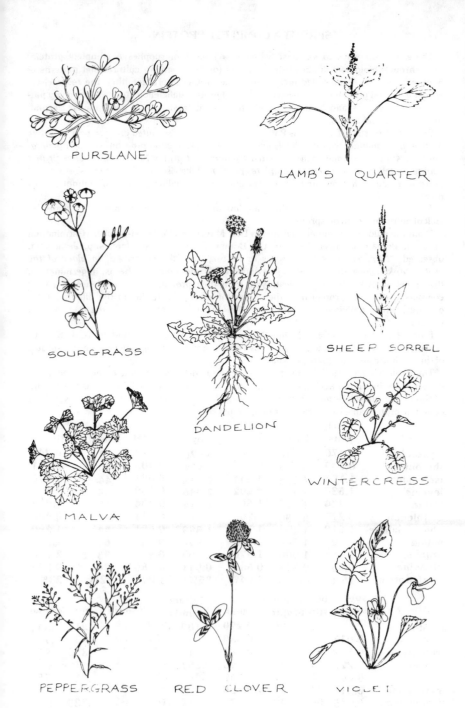

PURSLANE

LAMB'S QUARTER

SOURGRASS

DANDELION

SHEEP SORREL

MALVA

WINTERCRESS

PEPPERGRASS

RED CLOVER

VIOLET

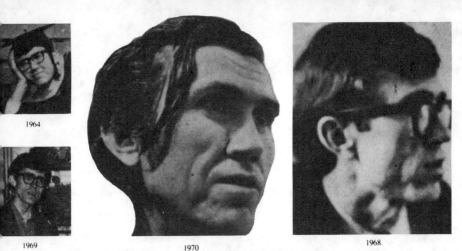

1964

1969

1970

1968

Viktoras goes through many changes because of the effect of live food.

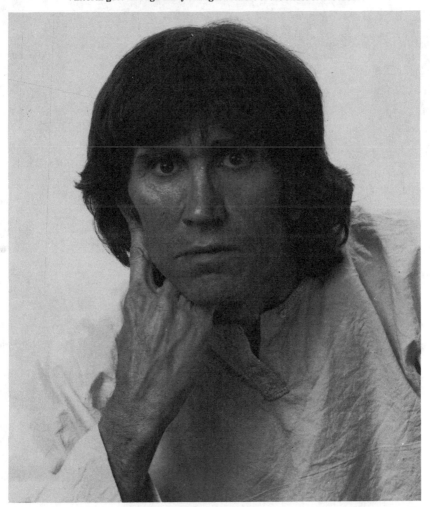

Viktoras, 1983, age 44. For learning more about the continued rejuvenation and dietary change experiences read *Survival Into 21st Century, Planetary Healers Manual*, pages 231 - 236.

Jacob's Ladder

SURVIVAL
Into The 21st Century

Cover: Peter Max; introduction: Dick Gregory

*Body Ecology, Spiritual Alchemy and Aquarian Eugenics.
Viktoras Peter Kulvinskas, M.S. Will you be alive in   1984?   2000?
2100? Are you healthy today?*

Read this manual for practical information on starting the path of natural living. Discover a healthful, youthful, spiritual, life style. Obtain organic food inexpensively. YOU CAN LIVE ON AN ALL ORGANIC FOOD DIET FOR LESS THAN $3.00 PER WEEK. Learn to recognize early warnings of impending chronic ailments, how to make a painless transition to a health-improving vegetarian diet to repair and maintain health.

This manual evaluates Kosher, vegetarian, macrobiotic, live food vegetarian, city fruitarian (SPROUTARIAN), liquitarian diet. Try a low protein, low starch, low fat, low mineral, high vitamin, high enzyme, live food diet for vitality, health, strength, endurance, regeneration, spirituality. Create a natural-normal child — a genious housed in a body of health and beauty.

How to become a Naturopath doctor (in the future there will be no need for this discipline — all will be beautiful and health); diagnosis, physiognomy, iridology, acupressure. Elimination of menstruation and menopause; continence; function of sex; breastfeeding; cause and elimination of cancer, diabetes, arthritis, hypoglycemia, szhizophrenia.

WHEATGRASS THERAPY for rejuvenation, correction of chronic ailments. WATER FAST for purification, heightened awareness, spiritual adventure. INDOOR ORGANIC GARDENING — grow all your food indoors in 7 days. SPROUTING — grow a complete meal in a jar, requiring only daily watering — one pound of seed produces seven pounds of sprouts. Prepare for FAMINE, STRIKES, REVOLUTION.

TASTY RECIPES arranged in health-promoting combinations. ACUPRESSURE (pressure message of feet) — for immediate relief of headache, constipation, dizziness. Complete loving body MASSAGE.

The processes of disease, NATURAL HEALING, fasting discussed at the cellular level for clear understanding of how disease is created and health regained. Appendix gives addresses for shopping by mail, health resorts, communes, New Age schools, directory of directories, reading list for continuing education.

Tropical colonization; grasses and sprouts for city survival; weed hunting and illustrations; food storage; selective non-organic food shopping. Build a $12 distiller, up to 4 gallons a day. Start an inexpensive organic restaurant.

Sunshine for lunch — breatharianiam; The temple of God and the river of Life; Cosmic forces of light and color therapy; Fruitarian aura; Nature of God; Structure of the Universe; The path of Yoga; Meditation; Karma; Reincarnation; Soul life.

The book reaches the inner person on the level of simplicity. IT IS THE FIRST REAL CHALLENGE AND AN ALTERNATIVE TO THE MACROBIOTIC. The book represents 4 years of preparation, which involved 2 years background study at Harvard Medical Library, self experimentation, plus observing the consequences and rejuvenation of others while acting as dietary "guru."

The book contains over 260 medical journal references. The appendix includes in excess of the following list of resources: 140 sources for seeds and fruit; 70 healing schools; 80 new age centers; 70 vegetarian activist groups; 250 books and reviews.

The first printing of *Survival* appeared Sept. 1975. The introduction is by Dick Gregory. Full color cover by Peter Max- the arrival of a cosmic being to the virgin planet earth. The back cover is by Jean White- the return to the Garden of Eden. She has included over 50 most beautiful visions, as well as many scientifically accurate physiological illustrations. Many photos of transformations. The text is 320 pages, 8 by 11, perfect bound paperback.

Author foresees a time when we will all be living in sunshine, love and eating from our own orchards. The smiling fruitarians will once again be the guru-priests, scientists to lead humanity back to god consciousness and joyful living.

The author was sick most of his life. At an early age was semi-conscious for many weeks from typhoid fever. By the age 29, he had suffered many years from ulcer, migraine, insomnia, acne, constipation, receding hairline and graying hair. His recovery to health centered on live food, juices, sprouts as well as rediscovery of a positive feeling toward self and others. In order to devote the time to helping others and study natural healing, he left behind the teaching of math (U-Conn) and computer programming. For over 7 years, he has participated in many capacities at the Hippocrates Health Institute, which included gardening, custodian service, research, lecturing, promotion, writing, publishing, as well as acting during the last few years as co-director. In 1975, he was invited to be a guest speaker at the World Vegetarian Conference, U-Maine. His ability with food preparations has been shown to be the strongest argument for vegetarianism. At most conventions, he was often refered to as the one from the "delicious booth."

YOU WILL ALSO WANT TO READ...

SURVIVAL INTO 21ST CENTURY. V Kulvinskas, Introduction by Dick Gregory, cover Peter Max and art by Jean White. **$21.95**

LIFE IN THE 21ST CENTURY, V. Kulvinskas. over 200 personal stories in the frontiers of live food nutrition and lifestyles. Reads like fiction but all true. 398 Pages **$14.95**

SPROUT FOR THE LOVE OF EVERYBODY , Kulvinskas M. S. Finally available a book that tells you about all the good things God has put into the seeds. Not only are sprouts packages of highest nutritional value but also source of predigested complete protein. Sprouts are good for all the zodiac signs, especially for those marked with cancer. New studies on cheap natural sources of chelated minerals, nucleic acids and their effect on rejuvenation. Studies on anemia, heart disorders, virility and survival. Many new methods of indoor gardening and sprouting. Illustrated and photos.
160 pgs, 4x7, **$8.95**

NEW AGE DIRECTORY, V. Kulvinskas. Over 2000 entries. Annotated. Indexed by subject, state and alphabet for easy referance The most detailed cover of healing, resorts, alternative nutritional oriented medical doctors, vegetarianism, fruitarianism, recreation, survival. **OUT OF PRI**

LIGHT EATING FOR SURVIVAL, Marcia Acciardo. Over 450 Raw food recipes: Pizza, breads, cakes, soups, seed cheeses and much more. **$14.00**

21ST CENTURY JOURNAL, Sproutarian network tool, published by Viktoras Kulvinskas; 48 page tabloid with eight regular editorials on subjects ranging from survival to herbology, astrology, and psychic healings. **OUT OF PRINT**

CATALOG; 12 page catalogue describing titles available from 21st Century Publications. Free.

Enclose check or money order plus 7½% postage and handling cost (minimum 75¢). 21st Century Publications, P.O. Box 702, Fairfield, Iowa 52556